The Living Pythons

Imperial Python, *Python boeleni.* Photo by R. D. Bartlett.

JERRY G. WALLS

TS-275

In memory of my mother
in her 85th year

Head and midbody view drawings by John Quinn. Hemipene drawings based on Dowling, 1975, and Branch, 1986.

CONTENTS

ACKNOWLEDGMENTS

Any large book is the result of more than just personal experience. It is based on a mixture of what has been published in the past, what you can learn from other people, and your own experiences and interpretations. Much of what has been written before is included in the bibliography (and the bibliographies included in many of those works), though there never has been a single comprehensive review of the pythons and their assorted baggage of related forms. My personal experience has been largely observational, and I've seen and handled a good percentage of the species of pythons recognized here. I must admit right at the beginning that I have never kept pythons because they are not compatible with my home life (a small house, small dogs, and other small pets), but this has not prevented me from enjoying them in the literature and as the pets of others.

I am greatly indebted to Dr. Darrel Frost and Margaret Arnold of the herpetology department at the American Museum of Natural History, New York, for allowing me access to the departmental reprint file and showing me the ins and outs of the Museum's library. My thanks also to Dr. Ken Williams, Northwestern State University, Natchitoches, Louisiana, for helping solve a couple of technical points, and to V. Wallach for some comments on Round Island snakes. The contributions of Drs. Samuel McDowell, Garth Underwood, and Arnold Kluge to the complex concepts of relationships among the pythons have been essential reading for this book, though I must admit that I have followed in detail none of their classifications. Paul Gritis, John Johnson, and Donald Hahn are just three of many book dealers who have provided numerous important papers and books making this particular book possible. Dick Bartlett provided answers to a few hands-on questions and gave of his usual encouragement.

I can't even begin to mention the many hobbyists and breeders who let me "take a look" at their snakes and answer a multitude of questions about their methods of keeping and breeding. A few of the many who stand out include Byron Barnes, Steve Ennis, Larry Kenton, Steve Mitchell and Satan, Steve Osborne, Dwayne Richard, and Jim Tracy. My wife, Maleta, took many photos of pythons at the various herp shows we attended in the Northeast, some used here but many even more important in supplementing the literature for details of scalation and color patterns.

The general hobbyist, in the zeal of attempting to add to the collection or perhaps breed a species for local sale, sometimes forgets just how important commercial breeders and dealers are to the herpetological hobby. Few hobbyists could afford the truly elite species and varieties of the pythons, but thanks to many men and women who devote countless, often thankless and low-paid, hours to making specimens available at reasonable prices, any hobbyist can gather a diverse collection of fine specimens. I hope that you will remember your local breeders and dealers as you pursue your hobby. And remember, captive-bred always is the best way to go.

A NOTE ON THE PAINTINGS

The color paintings of anterior, midbody, and ventral views of each python were done by John R. Quinn from the best descriptions and illustrations available, but they are still intended to be schematics, not scientifically detailed portraits. Pythons as a rule are highly variable snakes, so it is to be expected that individual specimens will differ to some extent from any painting or photograph.

Reticulated Python, *Python reticulatus*. Photo by R. D. Bartlett.

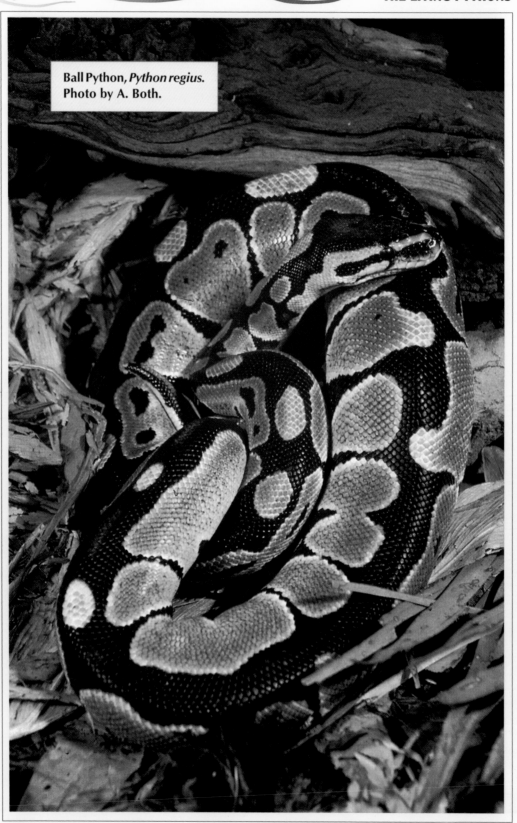

Ball Python, *Python regius.*
Photo by A. Both.

INTRODUCTION

There are few more spectacular animals than a 4-meter Burmese Python tamely being shown about by its owner. The larger pythons never fail to attract attention and give rise to a variety of reactions from repulsion and simple learned fear to delight in the ability to stroke and enjoy the skin texture of a truly unique animal. If you want to gather spectators around your table or counter at a show or in the pet shop, have someone take out even a 2-meter python and just stand back.

The pythons, including mostly the larger African, Asian, and Australian species, have been known to European man since the first reports filtered back from travelers in Asia and Africa of giant man-eating snakes. They have featured heavily in legend and myth, and perhaps even today the way most non-herpetologists think of pythons still could be called mythical. Though there is no doubt that a python occasionally will "take" (read this as "eat") a small human or cause the death of a careless handler, most pythons are small enough to not be a serious danger to humans under any circumstances. Only 10 or 12 species reach the length and bulk necessary to overpower a person (children included), but some of these are among the most commonly kept of the pythons. Though pythons can be wonderful pets if you have the facilities to house them correctly, some admittedly also are very dangerous animals.

The Living Pythons is half of a pair of volumes written with the intent to cover all the pythons and boas. At first it seemed that this would be a simple project, especially since there are fewer than 100 species recognized in total and there is a great deal of both technical and hobbyist literature on which to draw. However, I immediately ran across the problem of taxonomy versus classification. The pythons have been reviewed at the generic level three times in the last 20 years by vastly experienced anatomists and taxonomists. The three reviews bear almost no resemblance to each other in terms of generic groups recognized or even what snakes really are pythons. A somewhat similar situation exists in the boas. The problem is not so much the structure of the snakes, but a question of the philosophy that is used to interpret observations of a snake's structure. We'll go into this problem in more detail in the next chapter (which might be heavy slogging for many readers), but this might be the best place to define what I will call a "python" in this book.

Traditionally, pythons have been circularly defined as the members of the subfamily Pythoninae of the family Boidae. Unfortunately, this has proved to be a meaningless definition. For the purposes of this book, pythons are defined (in a rather free-form way) as several perhaps unrelated groups of boa-like (booid) snakes that lay eggs. They are a complex of several different families, each of which has retained the primitive character of laying eggs while modifying the body for various lifestyles from tree-dwelling to burrowing. The families included in this book are the **Pythonidae**, the true pythons of Africa, Asia, and Australia; **Calabariidae**, the Calabar or Burrowing Python of Africa; **Loxocemidae**, the Neotropical Python of Central America; the sunbeam snakes, **Xenopeltidae**, of southern Asia; and the truly unique relictual Round Island snakes, **Bolyeriidae**, known today only from Round Island in the Indian Ocean. In the following chapters I will try to define each of these families in words a hobbyist can understand and will describe and illustrate each of the species.

The pythons are a large and not homogeneous group (as recognized by the presence of several families) that stands in contrast to the differently specialized boas, here considered to be boa-like (booid) snakes that give live birth. For the purposes of this book the boas consist of three families: the true boas, **Boidae**, of Madagascar, the South Pacific, and tropical America; the burrowing boas, **Erycinidae**, of Africa, Asia, and North and Central America; and the dwarf boas or wood snakes, **Tropidophiidae**, of tropical America. These families will be covered in my other volume, *The Living Boas*.

The boas and pythons together are just part of a larger group of snakes that stand at a relatively primitive grade of structure compared to the colubrids or advanced snakes, family Colubridae in the broad sense. Other groups that at least in theory are not really distinguishable from the pythons and boas in the broad sense include the shield-tails, Uropeltidae, of Asia and the pipesnakes and kin, Aniliidae, of Asia and tropical America. Unfortunately, these families are even less well known than the boas and pythons in the broad sense and are very unfamiliar to hobbyists. As a matter of fact, two of the groups treated here as pythons (Loxocemidae and Xenopeltidae) often are considered to be aniliids and not in the boa and python lineage. As you might expect, the leading anatomists and taxonomists disagree about all features of classification of these snakes as well.

What you have to understand is that the technical classification of our snakes, whether at the family, genus, or species level, is in a constant state of flux, making familiar names almost meaningless.

There are many technical reasons for this, some of which we will discuss later, but the hobbyist must not allow confusion to interfere with the enjoyment of the hobby. Names are just means of communicating with other people and have no effect at all on the snakes. Just as there is no single correct way to pronounce a scientific name (regardless of what misguided zealots might tell you), it must be admitted that today there is no longer just one "correct" name for a snake. The concepts of genera, species, and subspecies are under attack from all sides, and the words no longer have common meanings to professional herpetologists. During this era of confusion, hobbyists perhaps have as much chance of being understood by using common names and descriptive phrases (a reversion to the type of scientific names used before the age of Linnaeus) as by following anyone's list of generic and specific Latin names. Later I will go through the motions of providing a uniform listing of scientific and common names because I am used to this type of identification, but be prepared to be confused a bit.

The plan of this book is simple and straightforward. I will cover each of the species of python in some detail, enough to allow it to be recognized and give the hobbyist (and scientist) an idea of its variability. The natural history and any odd details of terrarium care also will be covered. After this I'll discuss the broad outlines of python care and breeding. Though there are fewer than 40 species of pythons even in the broad sense that I've treated them in this book, there is enough diversity among them to make for some strange exceptions to the usual rules of captive care and breeding.

First and foremost, this is a book tailored to hobbyists. It might be a bit more technical than most books, but I think that it should allow you to answer most questions you have about pythons and also give you some different insights into the complexity of this particular group of snakes.

The rarely seen Angolan Python, *Python anchietae*. Photo by M. Burger.

The Green Tree Python, *P. viridis,* is often considered to belong to its own genus, but the evidence for this is scant. Photo by K. H. Switak.

PYTHONS AND CONTROVERSY

Because of their size and often formidable tempers, pythons are controversial pets. Later we will discuss some of the problems involved with keeping them safely in private hands (as opposed to zoos and large breeding establishments), but here I want to discuss another controversial aspect of the pythons: their classification. Distinguishing a python from a boa is a bit like telling a toad from a frog—it is strictly a matter of definition. The living snakes can be seen as occupying several distinct levels of structure, each level with a mixture of primitive and specialized characters. At the base are several families of wormsnakes or blindsnakes, such as the Typhlopidae and Leptotyphlopidae, that have many strange characters not found in other snakes. Above them comes a level with a mix of species that we call the boas, pythons, pipe snakes, shield-tails, and perhaps a couple of other groups. Above these are the colubrids or advanced snakes as well as the venomous snakes, the vipers and cobras and their allies. The booid [boa-like] level grades through certain families into the colubrid level, but most booids are relatively primitive, with many rows of scales around the body, narrow ventral scales, often primitive skull structure that may be modified considerably by adaptations to burrowing, often the presence of two distinct lungs (only a single well-developed lung in most colubrid level snakes), and a great number of very variable characters of the skeleton and soft parts (coronoid bone present, absent in colubrids; premaxillary teeth often present; postfrontal bone often present; keeled scales usually absent; hemipenes lacking spines; pupil of eye vertically elliptical; etc.).

FAMILIES

This book and the companion volume cover the pythons and boas, snakes of the booid level of development. Often all these snakes are treated as members of a single family, the Boidae, with numerous subfamilies. I feel that examination of the various reviews of the structure of these booid snakes leads to a different conclusion: the booids are members of several different families that show a varying mix of primitive and derived (specialized) characters. It is difficult or impossible to show that any one group is more closely related to and evolved from a second group than it is from any of the other groups. By recognizing each of the distinctive groups as a full family, the groups are put on a more even footing and there are no illusions about relationships that are not provable.

On this basis I recognize the booid level as containing about ten families:

Pipe snakes:
    Uropeltidae
    Aniliidae

Boas:
    Boidae
    Erycinidae
    Tropidophiidae

Pythons:
    Pythonidae
    Calabariidae
    Loxocemidae
    Xenopeltidae
    Bolyeriidae.

This book treats only the five families here called pythons, allied by laying eggs and usually having teeth on the premaxillary bones. I admit that this is a very artificial grouping, as the Loxocemidae and Xenopeltidae are just as close to the pipe snakes as to the boas and pythons, the Calabariidae is very similar in many respects to the Erycinidae (but in a recent DNA study clustered next to a uropeltid of all things!), and the Bolyeriidae is approaching the colubrid level and is similar in many respects to the Tropidophiidae. Because we are dealing with families with mixtures of characters and no distinct "direction" of evolution or specialization, the booid level cannot be represented as a regularly branching tree but instead is a multi-branched bush

with no distinct trunk.

Four of the five families are relatively easy to recognize and are very narrowly defined because they contain only one or two species. The Pythonidae has several distinctive characters, but in each case there is an exception to the character in the genus *Aspidites*, which assuredly is a true python but is either more primitive than the others or more specialized and has lost the characters (the latter situation being probable as the losses may be related to the burrowing habits of *Aspidites*). In the chapters that follow we will treat each family separately and attempt to define each in a general way to allow recognition by hobbyists. If you are interested in more technical characters for the various groups, please consult the papers in the bibliography, especially those by McDowell, Underwood, and Kluge.

GENERA

Within the Pythonidae, there is a tremendous disagreement about what genera are to be recognized as valid. At one extreme only three genera might be distinguished (*Python, Liasis, Aspidites*), while at another extreme there is evidence to recognize up to nine genera (*Antaresia, Apodora, Aspidites, Bothrochilus, Leiopython, Liasis, Morelia, Chondropython, Python*). In this book I've taken a compromise stand and recognized only four genera that are at least somewhat definable on the basis of structure as well as overall appearance. These are *Antaresia,*

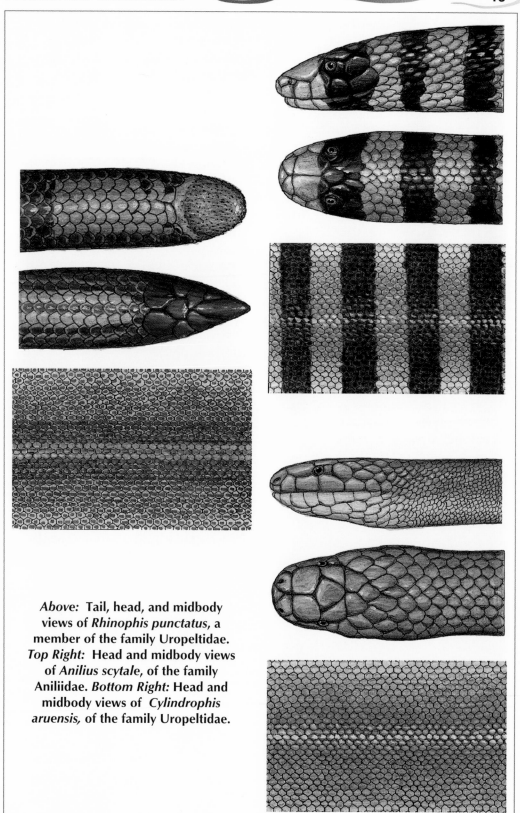

Above: Tail, head, and midbody views of *Rhinophis punctatus*, a member of the family Uropeltidae. *Top Right:* Head and midbody views of *Anilius scytale*, of the family Aniliidae. *Bottom Right:* Head and midbody views of *Cylindrophis aruensis*, of the family Uropeltidae.

Aspidites, Liasis, and *Python.* The other python families each have just one living genus, though the Bolyeriidae normally is considered to have two; in the discussion of that family I will synonymize the genus *Casarea* with the genus *Bolyeria.*

If you are aware of the current controversy between the traditional philosophy of taxonomy and classification and the relatively new methods of cladistics or phylogenetics, you might understand why there are so many different opinions in the scientific literature about families and genera of these snakes. In cladistics the aim is to construct a classification that shows the relationships of the animals contained in it, each category in the classification containing only animals derived from a common ancestor. A worker using the cladistic method records the degree of development of many characters or states, often between 50 and 100, including features from the skeleton, soft anatomy, superficial appearance, and biology of the animals. These states are rated by giving them numbers such as 0, 1, 2 (depending on presence, absence, or degree of development), and then fed into a computer program that compares the characters to each other and produces several to many branching charts or "phylogenetic trees" called cladograms. The researcher evaluates the cladograms and determines which is more likely to be "the" correct one. This cladogram then becomes the

basis of further discussions of relationships.

Cladists feel that their analyses are the only correct ones, but I personally cannot accept this position. In the first place, cladists feel that evolution acts in a direct and simple way, so the best cladograms are the ones that take the fewest steps to get from group A to group B. This is the principle of parsimony, the belief that nature always takes the shortest way to solve a problem. Unfortunately, the world around us shows that this is not correct, and nature often seems to take very round-about ways of producing new animals. Additionally, by coding all characters of an animal in a simple fashion, all characters are treated as though they were of equal significance. I just do not believe that this is a correct interpretation of nature; some characters are more important in determining relationships than are others. In the pythons, for instance, the scales or shields of the head are notoriously variable and cannot be used to define groups above the specific level unless accompanied by other characters, yet in several cladistic classifications head scales are given equal value to features of the skull and skeleton in determining relationships. Finally, a computer program may produce literally dozens of differing cladograms from the same information, and it is the researcher, with all his or her acknowledged or subconscious biases, who in the end tells us which is the "correct" cladogram. To the computer all the dozens of cladograms are equally correct interpretations of the data, and it finally is the beliefs of the researcher in interpreting the cladograms that determine what genera are recognized.

The traditional methods of taxonomy were more practical, using analyses of structure and distribution to produce groups of similar-appearing animals. If there was a gap in the characters setting one group apart from another, the groups were termed genera and assumed to be composed of related species. Differences and gaps formed the basis of the classification. When species were discovered that bridged the gap between established genera, the genera were reassessed and usually one was made a synonym of the other (though occasionally a new genus was erected for the intermediate species). The traditional system was "relationship neutral" in that you could use the classifications without worrying about how the animals had evolved and without having to answer the questions about which groups were related to or derived from which other groups. This made it a practical system and one making identification easier.

I tend to follow the traditional philosophy because I believe that classifications at the generic level must be practical: they must make it possible to more easily identify animals. The entire Linnean system was developed to make identification easy and practical, and I feel that still should be its purpose.

The relationship of the Calabar Python, *Calabaria reinhardti,* to the other pythons remains controversial. Photo by P. J. Stafford.

Although many hobbyists place the Carpet Python in the genus *Morelia*, here it is considered a member of the genus *Python*, *P. spilotus variegatus*. Photo by V. T. Jirousek.

Complicated philosophies of relationships and evolution are not necessary when constructing a taxonomy of a group, and they probably are wrong as well because there never is sufficient information to really know for sure how an animal evolved. The fossil record of snakes, for instance, consists mostly of vertebrae that, regardless of what the experts opine, almost certainly cannot be used to trace relationships, just modifications of a single rather simple structure. Genera are artificial groups anyway, at least in my philosophy, and they do not evolve; only species evolve.

SPECIES

What is a species? Frankly, I don't know and neither does anyone else. Definitions have been given for over 300 years and still don't answer the basic question. Older definitions that once were standard, including those that required lack of interbreeding between related species, largely have gone by the board. In fact, some biologists believe that hybridization or intergradation either in nature or in the laboratory is meaningless in determining relationships, and they probably are right. (In this philosophy the ability to interbreed is of course a primitive character, and one cannot base classifications on shared primitive characters.)

In this book I've tried to follow or at least give lip service to my interpretation of a rather new but very simple concept of species that also is quite practical. (See Wiley, 1978, for the first full discussion of the evolutionary species concept.) Basically, a species is defined as **a population of similar animals that are isolated (geographically, behaviorally, or biochemically) from other populations, are differentiated at some level, and have their own evolutionary history.** Differences between species may not always be visible to the human eye—after all, we cannot hear, see, and smell what a snake thinks to be of importance in defining its own kind. We know that there are distinct species of treefrogs that can be distinguished only by calls, species of insects that are separated by differences in timing of the life cycle, and many

Many scientists do not recognize *Antaresia* as distinct from *Liasis*. This is the Blotched Python, *A. stimsoni*. Photo by Z. Takacs.

different animals that differ in minor details of breeding biology, including hormones and scent secretions. With new biochemical techniques it is possible to determine the genetic similarities—and differences—of two groups of animals to a very fine point. In the near future it should be economically realistic to conduct biochemical tests on numerous individuals from throughout the range of every possibly distinct population of python and actually see how closely related each is to the other. Until then, we just have to look at the structure and distribution and take an educated guess.

In practical terms, a species of python is any isolated group of animals that no longer seems to be sharing genes with its close relatives and thus has begun on its own evolutionary path, **and** has progressed far enough down this path to show distinctions of some type. Simple isolation, as on an island or on the opposite sides of a busy highway, is not sufficient to indicate the animals are a species. After all, pythons commonly swim good distances across shallow (and sometimes open) seas, so there is no reason to automatically assume that island animals are isolated. They must show signs that they have not shared genes with other animals long enough ago that they have begun their own history. This may be strongly indicated by differences in color pattern or scale counts as compared to the close relatives. A group (population) of animals in, for instance, southwestern

Australia, isolated from its closest relatives by hundreds of kilometers and showing differences in scale counts or color patterns, will automatically be treated as a full species if it has been formally named in the past.

On the other hand, if two distinctive-appearing groups of pythons are not isolated and appear (from the nature of their variation) to be sharing genes, they are not species no matter how distinctive they may seem to human eyes. Remember that humans are visually oriented—we **see** differences; most other animals, including pythons, probably **smell** differences. If we try to apply human-made distinctions to non-human animals we probably will be wrong.

A final word on hybridization. The fact that two well-differentiated species exchange genes over a narrow band or fragment where their ranges overlap is not an indication of less than specific status. Such limited hybridization may be a natural way of actually increasing the distinction between species, the hybrids serving as a barrier to prevent spreading of genes further into the parent populations. Many very different animals hybridize regularly in nature (for instance, the very different Mallard and Pintail ducks) and certainly are full species, often in different species groups. Natural hybridization must be carefully

Reticulated Pythons, *P. reticulatus,* could be considered members of *Morelia* by some taxonomists. Photo by K. T. Nemuras.

PYTHON STRUCTURE AND A CHECKLIST

FINDING YOUR WAY AROUND A PYTHON

As you quickly will notice, this book is one largely of identification and description. As such, it uses many terms that may not be too familiar to you. To go into details on the structure of any snake would require a full book, one that admittedly has never been written and is sorely needed. I hope that the following quick summary will give you enough information to be able to follow the descriptions and understand what are the important features in identifying a python.

In case you don't know the basic scientific directions, **anterior** refers to going toward the front, **posterior** means going toward the back, and **lateral** going toward the side. **Dorsal** refers to the back or top of a structure or body, while **ventral** refers to the bottom or undersurface (belly) of a body or structure. The different directions can be combined, as in

Here an amelanistic Burmese Python, *P. molurus bivittatus,* displays both its forked tongue and heat-sensitive labial pits. Photo by K. H. Switak.

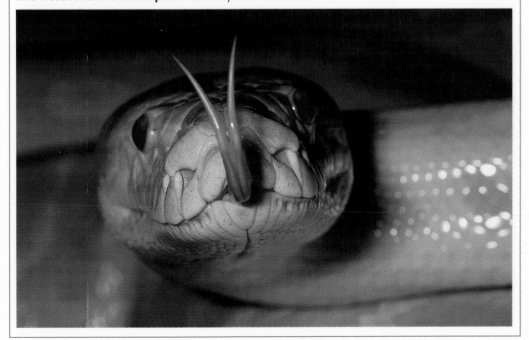

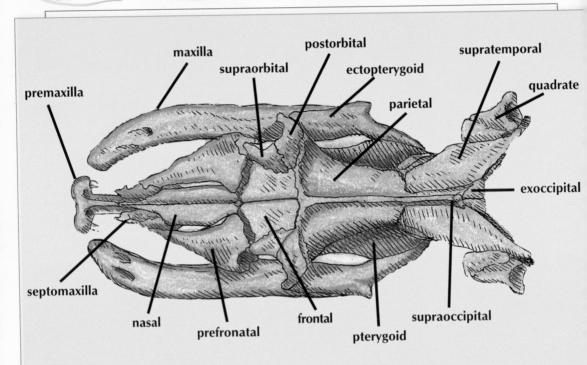

Dorsal view of skull of *Python sebae*. Based on Frazzetta, 1959. *Bull. Mus. Comp. Zool.*, 119 (8).

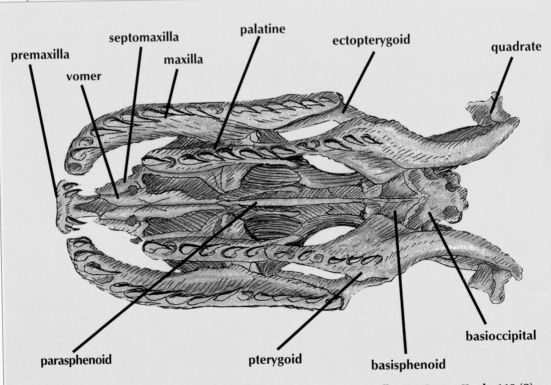

Ventral view of skull of *Python sebae*. Based on Frazzetta, 1959. *Bull. Mus. Comp. Zool.*, 119 (8).

ventrolateral. Distal refers to a direction away from the origin or base of a structure, while proximal refers to going toward the base.

The Skull

The skull is of course the skeleton forming the head of a snake. Technically, what usually is called the skull is the cranial skeleton, comprising the lower jaws or mandibles and the upper jaws and braincase, the skull proper. If you look at the skull of a typical python from above, the rather T-shaped bone that is at the front of the skull is the **premaxillary**, formed by the fusion of a left and a right element. Behind the premax the paired and rather elongated bones forming the central part of the skull are the **nasals**. They are flanked by large **prefrontals** on either side. The prefrontals join the anterior edges of the **frontal**

bones, which usually are paired and occupy the center of the skull. To either side of the frontals are the indentations for the eyes, the orbits. The tops of the orbits usually are covered by a hooked bone called the **postorbital**. In the true pythons there is a small, rather plain bone preceding the postorbital that forms the anterior part of the upper orbit. This is the **postfrontal** or supraorbital, characteristic of the Pythonidae. The bones of the top of the skull behind the level of the eyes are the **parietals**. The long bone that allows the jaws to expand, the **supratemporal**, is attached by ligaments to the parietal on each side. The other bones of the back and interior of the skull don't feature in the descriptions used in this book and won't be mentioned.

When you look at the skull from below, you notice that there are several rows of teeth, usually two

Lateral view of skull of *Python sebae.* Based on Frazzetta, 1959. *Bull. Mus. Comp. Zool.,* 119 (8)

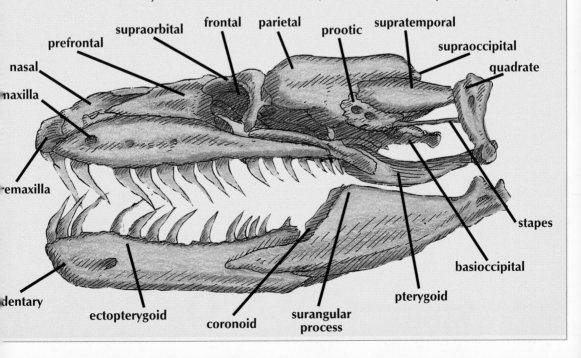

on each side and one across the front. Taken in order, the row across the front is the **premaxillary row**, usually one to three teeth placed in clusters on either side of the premaxillary bone. Around the outside of the skull is the row of **maxillary teeth**, which in pythons often contains over a dozen teeth, the anterior ones long and curved backward. The final sets of teeth are on two separate bones that are joined and run in rows closer to the center of the skull. These teeth are on the roof of the mouth and without cleaning off some tissue appear to be one continuous row on each side. Actually, the longer anterior teeth are on the **palatine** bone, while the shorter ones to the back are on the **pterygoid.**

The lower jaw is the **mandible**, and it is a composite comprising three major bones visible from the outside. The mandibular teeth are borne on the **dentary**. The back part of the mandible is the **surangular**, while the **coronoid** bone is a small bone on the "hump" near the center of the jaw. The surangular attaches to the supratemporal bone by the **quadrate** bone, allowing great expansion of the jaws to swallow prey.

Head Scales

Pythons are more variable in scalation characters than are more "advanced" snakes, but the scales of the head and body still are of extreme importance in identification. The enlarged scales of the head often are called shields to distinguish them from the body scales.

The tip of the snout is covered by the **rostral** shield or scale. The nostrils are in the **nasal** shields, which in pythons usually are each a single scale with a seam or suture that fails to split the nasal into two pieces. Between the nasals at the end of the snout are the usually squarish and rather small **internasals.** Behind the internasals are the paired (usually) **prefrontals**, which vary from one to three pairs, but usually only the anterior pair is large and elongated. Between the eyes across the top of the head are three shields. In the center is the **frontal**, which varies from somewhat triangular to oval or squarish or many-sided. On each side of the frontal over the eyes are the **supraoculars.** In many pythons the supraocular on each side is a single large scale, but in many others it is split or fragmented into two, three, or occasionally more smaller scales. The front edge of the frontal contacts the prefrontals, while the back edge commonly contacts a pair of enlarged scales called the **parietals**. There may be several pairs of parietals or just small scales like the others on the nape of the neck.

From the side, the nasal shields are prominent. In front of the eye are one to several large scales called the **preoculars.** Between the nasal shield and the preoculars are one to 20 or more **loreal** scales. Often the loreals are of mixed sizes, some being large and others small or even just

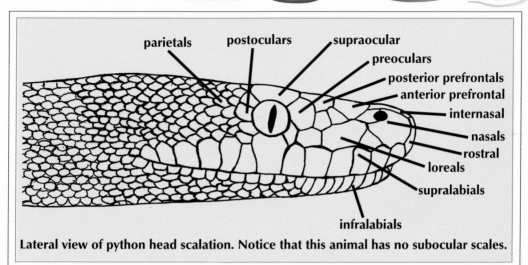

Lateral view of python head scalation. Notice that this animal has no subocular scales.

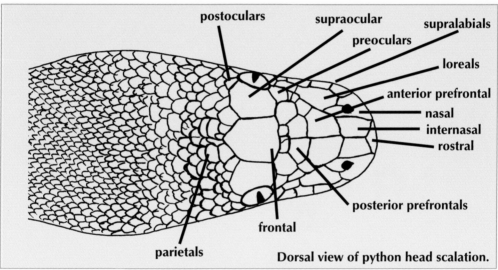

Dorsal view of python head scalation.

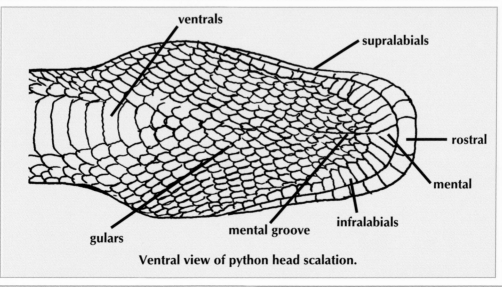

Ventral view of python head scalation.

Head view of the Island Water Python, *Liasis mackloti*. Photo by W. P. Mara.

granules (granular scales). The loreals usually are bordered above by the prefrontals. Behind the eye is a row of one to five or six scales called the **postoculars**. The scales behind these are the **temporals**, which are not used in descriptions in this book.

The scales forming the edge of the upper lip are the **supralabials**; those forming the edge of the lower lip are the **infralabials**. It often is important to notice how many supralabials touch the lower edge of the eye. Such supralabials often are said to form the lower margin of the **orbit** or to enter the eye. From below, the infralabials on each side meet at the front of the jaw on either side

of a single scale called the mental. In most pythons there is a deep groove running down the center of the throat, the mental groove, that allows the jaws to stretch to swallow large prey. Often the groove is bordered by one or two pairs of enlarged scales called the **gulars**. In most pythons the gulars are small and not strongly distinguished from the other scales under the jaw; usually only one pair of gulars is really enlarged. In *Python viridis* the scales bordering the groove are granular, and in some pythons the groove is absent or indistinct.

Body Scales

In pythons the scales usually

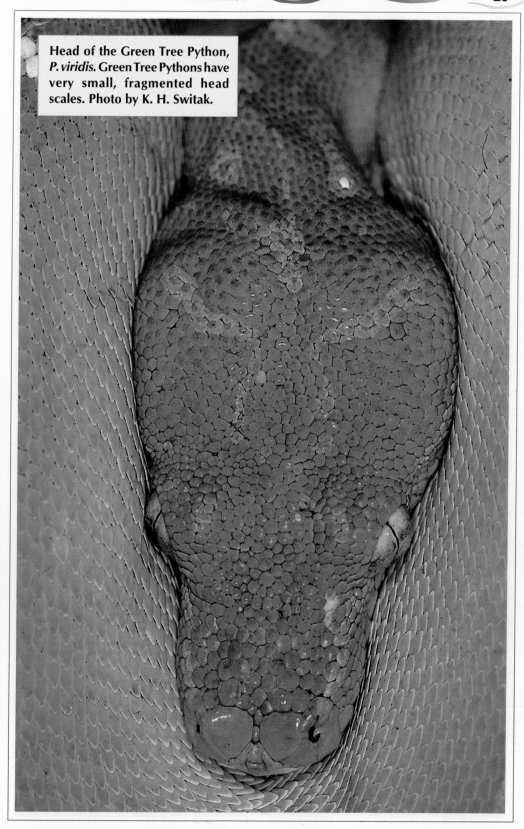

Head of the Green Tree Python, *P. viridis.* Green Tree Pythons have very small, fragmented head scales. Photo by K. H. Switak.

The expandable skin on the mouth and throat of pythons is visible on this Black-headed Python, *Aspidites melanocephalus*. Photo by R. Kayne.

L. fuscus Peters, 1873
  Australian Water Python
L. mackloti Dumeril & Bibron, 1844
  Island Water Python
L. olivaceus Gray, 1842
  Olive Python
L. papuanus Peters & Doria, 1878
  Papuan Python
L. savuensis Brongersma, 1956
  White-eyed Water Python
Python Daudin, 1803
P. amethistinus (Schneider, 1801)
  Scrub Python
P. anchietae Bocage, 1887
  Angolan Python
P. boeleni (Brongersma, 1953)
  Imperial Python
P. bredli Gow, 1981
  Bredl's Python
P. carinatus L. A. Smith, 1981
  Rough-scaled Python
P. curtus Schlegel, 1872
  Blood Python
P. imbricatus L. A. Smith, 1981
  Southwestern Carpet Python
P. molurus (Linnaeus, 1758)
  Asian Rock Python
P. natalensis (A. Smith, 1840)
  Lesser Rock Python
P. oenpelliensis Gow, 1977
  Oenpelli Python
P. regius (Shaw, 1802)
  Ball Python
P. reticulatus (Schneider, 1801)
  Reticulated Python
P. sebae (Gmelin, 1789)
  African Rock Python
P. spilotus (Lacepede, 1804)
  Common Carpet Python
P. timoriensis (Peters, 1876)
  Timor Python
P. viridis Schlegel, 1872
  Green Tree Python

Family LOXOCEMIDAE Cope, 1861
Loxocemus Cope, 1861
L. bicolor Cope, 1861
  Neotropical Python
Family XENOPELTIDAE Bonaparte, 1846
Xenopeltis Reinwardt in Boie, 1827
X. hainanensis Hu & Zhao, 1972
  Hainan Sunbeam Snake
X. unicolor Reinwardt in Boie, 1827
  Common Sunbeam Snake
Family CALABARIIDAE Underwood, 1976
Calabaria Gray, 1858
C. reinhardti (Schlegel, 1851)
  Calabar Python
Family BOLYERIIDAE Hoffstetter, 1946
Bolyeria Gray, 1842
B. dussumieri (Schlegel, 1837)
  Slender Split-jaw
B. multocarinata (Boie, 1827)
  Burrowing Split-jaw

Scrub Pythons, *P. amethistinus,* are among the longest of all snakes. Photo by V. Jirousek.

The Rough-spotted Python, *Antaresia maculosa,* is fairly common on the American reptile market. Photo by J. Coborn.

AUSTRALASIAN PYTHONS, FAMILY PYTHONIDAE

There are three genera of pythons that are distributed exclusively in Australia and New Guinea (plus the Flores). One of these, *Aspidites*, is extremely distinct in structure, lacking premaxillary teeth and thermosensory pits on the labial scales; its two species are restricted to Australia. There have been arguments for years as to whether *Aspidites* is a primitive relative to the other pythons or extremely specialized for burrowing, in the process losing the premaxillary teeth and labial pits. (To me these pythons look like very modified derivatives of *Python amethistinus*.) The four species of *Antaresia* (all Australian) are a small but distinctive group of spotted pythons that seldom reach a meter in length. Additionally, they have a full complement of head shields, shallow pits in the infralabials, and a distinctive group of a few large and several small loreal scales. With the genus *Liasis* we have a group of very similar large, glossy brown (or black and orange) pythons with fully developed head shields, shallow pits in the infralabials and usually one or more of the first three supralabials, and one or at most two loreal scales. They could be confused with *Python* species with complete head scales, but in addition to usually reduced supralabial pitting and a single loreal, they have pits on the posterior dorsal scales and lack a prehensile tail (a character that can only be observed in life).

Liasis often has been defined to include the species of *Antaresia* or has been partitioned into as many as four genera for the five or six species traditionally placed in *Liasis* without *Antaresia*. (I recognize eight species of *Liasis* here, elevating two isolated and differentiated subspecies to species rank.) In the extreme generic splitting proposed by Kluge (1993), you would have: *Bothrochilus [boa]; Leiopython [albertisi]; Liasis [mackloti, olivaceus, fuscus, savuensis, barroni];* and *Apodora [papuana].* I find this system impossible to follow because it would separate closely related species into separate genera (*olivaceus* and *papuanus; albertisi* and *boa*), obscuring relationships. The species of *Liasis* form a very uniform group in both external and internal characters, the differences between the species not being of a much greater level than between the species of African and southern Asian

White-lipped Pythons, *Liasis albertisi*, are treated here as *Liasis*, not *Leiopython*, which is commonly used in the hobby. Photo by I. Francais.

pythons, and not as much as between the *molurus* and *reticulatus* groups of *Python*. My personal philosophy is to recognize broad genera with more finely split species, and I do not recognize *Bothrochilus*, *Leiopython*, or *Apodora*, treating them as synonyms of *Liasis*.

KEY TO THE GENERA OF PYTHONIDAE

A. Supralabial and infralabial sensory pits completely absent; head shields fully developed; one to three loreals...............*Aspidites*

AA. At least one supralabial or infralabial with a sensory pit; head scales fully developed to fragmented; often more than four loreals...B

B. A single supralabial shallowly pitted and several posterior infralabials pitted; head shields fully developed; loreal region typically with one to four larger and two to six (or more) small scales; small spotted pythons..........................*Antaresia*

BB. Not with the above combination of characters..........C

C. One (rarely two) enlarged loreal; head shields fully developed; supralabial row with no to three sensory pits, no more than one or two deep; glossy brown with or without small pale spots or ringed black and orange; tail not prehensile.............*Liasis*

CC. Three to 20+ loreals; head shields fully developed to completely fragmented except for the internasals; supralabial row with either two or three deep sensory pits; body almost always with a distinct dark and light pattern (rarely glossy black with yellow stripes or bright green); tail prehensile..........................*Python*

Genus *Antaresia* Wells & Wellington, 1983[=1984](*Aust. J. Herp.*, 1[3-4]: 105). Type species *Nardoa gilbertii* Gray = *childreni* Gray.

Synonyms: None.

Though the validity of the generic name has been questioned because of the way it was described (Australian herpetologists attempted to have at least traces of four rows of brownish spots or blotches. The rostral scale lacks pits, the first one or two supralabials may be shallowly pitted, and the posterior infralabials are pitted. The head scales are distinct and well-formed, and there are two or three pairs of prefrontals. The loreals number from three or four to 20 or so and often consist of a row of small scales above the supralabials and larger scales above them. The tail is

Antaresia has heavy pits on the posterior infralabials, seen here in the Blotched Python, *A. stimsoni.* Photo by Z. Takacs.

the entire *Australian Journal of Herpetology*, a privately produced effort that often failed to take scientific procedures seriously, banned and all the new names proposed in it stricken from the scientific record), *Antaresia* is a validly described genus and its four species form a very tight-knit group of similar species.

Antaresia comprises small pythons seldom reaching a meter in length and always marked with moderately long, to about 14% of the total length, and the scales at midbody are in fewer than 50 rows.

KEY TO THE SPECIES OF ANTARESIA

A. Adults with dark spots or blotches strongly defined and distinct from background..........B

AA. Adults with dark spots poorly defined from background or superficially absent................C

B. Blotches on back dark

chocolate-brown, of varied sizes, and with especially jagged and irregular edges; blotches tend to fuse into short wavy stripes on the sides; dorsal scales in 34 to 44 rows at midbody; ventrals 246 to 287.................................*maculosa*

BB. Blotches on back reddish brown to dark brown, tending to form smooth-edged ovals or enlarged transverse bands; a white stripe often visible above the ventrals; dorsal scales in 36 to 47 rows at midbody; ventrals 243 to 284.................................*stimsoni*

C. Dorsal spots sandy brown to pale brown, sometimes with a purplish tinge, and usually visible in adults; dorsal scales in 36 to 46 rows at midbody; ventrals 251-300.................................*childreni*

CC. Dorsal spots often not visible against reddish brown back in adults; dorsal scales in 31 to 35 rows at midbody; ventrals 212-250..........*perthensis*

The four species of *Antaresia* may be difficult to distinguish, and they are badly confused in the scientific and hobbyist literature. Though it is not entirely satisfactory, I've followed L. A. Smith's 1985 review of the group (*Rec. West. Aust. Mus.*, 12(2): 257-276) for details and used his names for the species. There still are several questions to be answered, and there is no proven isolation between the various species. Where the range of *A. stimsoni* comes into near contact with the ranges of *A. childreni* and *A. maculosa*, specimens may not be distinguishable, and there is considerable evidence for narrow hybrid zones between these species.

Hobbyists long have lumped three of the species (all except *A. perthensis*) under the name *childreni* and used the common name Children's Python for this composite concept of the species. Because of the confusion in using the name Children's Python, I will not be using it in this book. Instead, the name Faded Python, in use among some hobbyists and very appropriate, is used for *A. childreni.*

ANTARESIA CHILDRENI
Faded Python

The Faded Python is one of the most commonly seen forms of the genus and often is illustrated. It is a slender, cylindrical python with a widened head distinct from the neck. At first glance it resembles a colubrid snake or a wood snake (*Tropidophis*). The eye is golden and quite distinct though small.

Description

From above, the snout is rather narrow or conical and rounded, the rostral narrowly visible from above. The internasals are large and roughly squarish. There is a pair of large anterior prefrontals and a smaller pair of posterior prefrontals. The posterior prefrontals may be in contact or more often separated by a few small scales, and occasionally they are split to produce two distinct pairs of posterior prefrontals. The frontal is

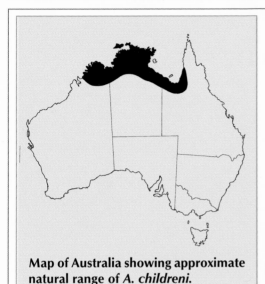

Map of Australia showing approximate natural range of *A. childreni*.

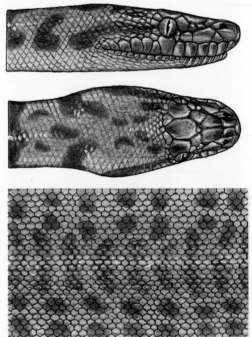

Head and midbody views of *A. childreni*.

squarish to triangular and may be separated from the prefrontals by small scales. A pair of parietals usually is distinct. From the side, the nostrils are generally lateral in position and the nasal scale is separated from the preoculars by about four to 16 loreals, typically eight, of mixed sizes. There are two preoculars, a large upper one and a small lower one that sometimes is counted as a loreal. There usually are three or four postoculars. The 10 to 16 supralabials bear a shallow pit in the first (sometimes another in the second) supralabial, and two supralabials enter the lower margin of the eye. There are 12 to 16 infralabials, three to seven posterior ones bearing shallow pits.

The dorsal scales are in 36 to 46 rows at midbody; there are 24 to 39 one head length behind the head and 19 to 29 one head length before the vent. The ventrals number 251 to 300, and there are 38 to 57 pairs (mostly) of subcaudals.

The hemipenes are bilobate, shallowly forked, with very short papillae (awns) at the tips of the lobes. There are only two flounces on the organ. The male hemipene pouches will probe about 10 to 12 subcaudals.

The overall color of the Faded Python is a pale sandy to muddy brown, the belly white. The top of the head is pale brown and bears a few poorly defined darker spots and blotches. There is a dark stripe from the nostril through the eye to the back of the head, and the upper lip has short vertical dark bars and a dark stripe posteriorly. The body may be without an obvious spotted pattern or may have more than 70 series of small, clean-edged darker muddy brown spots and blotches in about four rows, the

A. *childreni,* like most pythons, will climb from time to time and should be housed with a branch or two. Photo by K. H. Switak.

lowest row not reaching the ventrals. The blotches often are fused into short bars. Both spotted and plain specimens may occur in the same population. Many specimens have a distinct purplish tinge especially visible posteriorly. This species is never chocolate brown or dark reddish brown in color.

Typical adult Faded Pythons are 60 or 70 cm in total length, but there are records of a few specimens reaching and exceeding a meter.

Natural Variation

As noted, there is considerable variation in pattern, though the muddy brown color is constant. Young specimens tend to be strongly spotted, but with growth the spots fade, becoming softer and less contrasting and showing a tendency to fuse into short bars. Specimens lacking dorsal spots are not necessarily the oldest specimens, and spotted and plain specimens of the same size and probable age occur in the same areas. The sexes are not distinguishable externally.

In northern Western Australia and southern Northern Territory specimens intermediate between the Faded Python and Blotched Python may represent hybrids.

Natural History

The Faded Python is a species of northern Australia, ranging from the Kimberley region of northern Western Australia through the northern part of the Northern Territory and into northwestern Queensland. It also occurs on many islands off the Australian coast. Through this rather small range it occurs in almost all available habitats, from closed wet forests through open scrub to caves and crevices in sandstone cliffs.

It is active at night and feeds on a tremendous variety of prey, from frogs and lizards to small mammals and birds. It survives well in proximity to man, probably because of its small size and ability to live off so many types of food. Faded Pythons are gentle animals that seldom bite, but they do have a full share of teeth and are not afraid to use them if cornered or attacked.

In nature mating appears to take place during the Australian winter (June through August), with eggs being laid in September and October. The eggs are small, only 40mm long, and the hatchlings are about 250 to 275mm long. Hatchlings feed on small lizards, especially skinks and geckos.

Husbandry

The Faded Python does well in captivity, and because of its small size and relatively sluggish habits it can live in a small terrarium. It does not need excessively warm temperatures but does like a warm basking area. Most specimens will feed on small mammals and chicks, but they also like the occasional lizard tidbit. Faded Pythons and other *Antaresia* may live for over 20 years in captivity.

Breeding still is difficult, but a good number of young are produced each year in the United States and Europe. As with most pythons, mating is encouraged by separating the sexes and cooling them a bit for a month or two during the (northern) winter while shortening the day length and reducing the food. Always give a water bowl. A temperature of about 21°C (70°F) works well. After the cool period the sexes are put together (males sometimes fight, so use only one male per group of females) and mating should occur.

Clutches are of about three to 20 adherent white eggs with delicate shells. The female, as always, broods the eggs, but usually they are removed to a

Hatchling Faded Pythons have a more distinct pattern than the adults. Photo by W. P. Mara.

relatively dry incubator for the about 50 days required for hatching. The best incubation temperature, as for most pythons, is about 32°C (90°F). The hatchling's are small and may demand small skinks as a first food. Some immediately feed on mice, but others may have to be force-fed or tried on mice rubbed on a lizard for scenting or doused with a concoction of minced lizard in water.

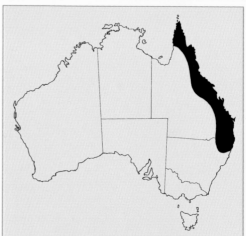

Map of Australia showing general natural range of *A. maculosa*.

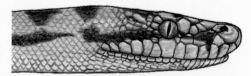

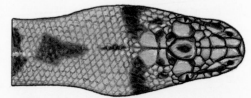

Due to their small size and docile temperament, Faded Pythons make good snakes for beginning keepers. Photo by R. D. Bartlett.

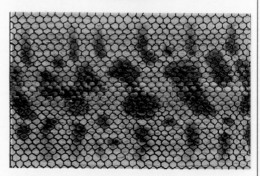

Head and midbody views of *A. maculosa*.

Taxonomic History

Gray (*Zool. Misc.*: 44) described *Liasis childreni* from an unknown locality. In the same paper (page 45) he also described *Nardoa gilberti* from Port Essington in northern Australia. Almost from the beginning these two names were considered to represent a single species. Boulenger's *Catalogue* (1893) states that the type specimen of *childreni* came from N.W. Australia. Gray's *childreni* represents the oldest name in the genus.

ANTARESIA MACULOSA
Rough-spotted Python

The Rough-spotted Python is in many respects intermediate between the Faded Python and the Blotched Python, though it

A. perthensis hails from the deserts of the Pilbara region, dwelling near termite mounds, which are called anthills by the local Australians. Photo by R. Hoser.

the two species appear to overlap in distribution along the coast.

A nocturnal species, it feeds mostly on lizards but also takes some small mammals. Many species die crossing the roads at night, but the species is fully protected from collecting and thus hard to maintain legally in the hobby. Numbers can be found associated with the large free-standing termite mounds (anthills in Aussie-speak) that dot the Western Australian dry scrubland. It's habitat generally consists of reddish sands and spinifex grasses.

Husbandry

This species rarely is kept in captivity because of Australian laws. However, it is known to lay small clutches (fewer than five eggs) of large white eggs (about 40 X 25mm) and to brood the clutch. Hatchlings are only 170 to 180mm long, truly tiny pythons. They must be fed on lizards and lizard tails until they are large enough to take pinkie mice. Anthill Pythons still are common, and if Australian laws ever change they should make good terrarium pythons.

Taxonomic History

Stull described *Liasis perthensis* in 1932 from a specimen supposed to be from Perth in southwestern Western

Australia, an area where the species does not occur (*Occas. Papers Boston Soc. Nat. Hist.*, No. 8: 26). L. A. Smith (1985) reviewed the species. It appears to be the most distinctive species of the genus and the only one that does not hybridize in nature with an ally.

ANTARESIA STIMSONI
Blotched Python

When L. A. Smith described this new species in 1985, he helped to clarify variation in the *Antaresia* species but at the same time created a taxonomically questionable situation of species

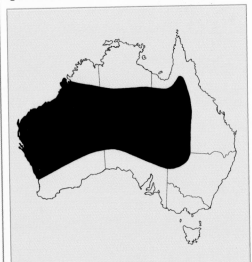

Map of Australia showing natural range of *A. stimsoni.*

(and subspecies) that were defined on weakly developed color characters and tendencies in scale counts.

Description

In general shape and appearance this species is very similar to the Faded Python. There are two or three pairs of prefrontals, the posterior prefrontals often separated at the midline by a few small scales. There are about a dozen loreals of mixed sizes and usually four or five postoculars. The supralabials number 11 to 15, the first and sometimes second with shallow pits and two entering the lower margin of the eye. There are 12 to 16 infralabials, some of the posterior ones pitted.

There are about 40 to 47 scale rows at midbody (31 to 42 one head length behind the head and 24 to 28 one head length before the vent) in the western part of the range and 36 to 45 in the eastern part of the range. The ventrals in the western part of the range are 260 to 302 (mean about 280), while there are 243 to 284 (mean 264) to the east. The subcaudals (mostly divided)

Head and midbody views of *A. stimsoni.*

This *A. stimsoni* has enlarged parietal scales, a very unusual trait in this genus. However, it is common for python head scales to vary greatly between individuals. Photo by R. D. Bartlett.

number 40 to 55 (mean 46) in the west and 38 to 53 (mean 43) in the east.

Blotched Pythons are pale to medium tan with many large, even-edged spots or blotches of dark chocolate brown. In the western part of the range the animals often appear rather subdued and muddy in color, the pattern consisting mostly of round or elongated blotches. At the eastern edge of the range the snakes tend to be more crisply colored, with large blotches extending over most of the back and in strong contrast. The head tends to have many dark spots and the usual dark stripes through the eye and on the posterior upper lip. Typically there is a distinct narrow white stripe above the ventrals on the lower side at least anteriorly (absent or very poorly defined in the related species).

Adults are small but average a bit longer than the other species of the genus at about 600 to 850mm. The record for the species seems to be 1270mm total length.

Natural Variation

When Smith described this species he described two subspecies, an eastern (*stimsoni orientalis*) and a western (*stimsoni stimsoni*). The two differed in tends of counts, with a few more middorsal scales, ventrals, and subcaudals in western specimens than eastern ones, and larger and more colorful blotches in the east than the west. The two subspecies do not have discrete

This is a typical Blotched Python. At the borders of their ranges, the species of *Antaresia* hybridize (except *perthensis*), making identification extremely difficult. Photo by R. D. Bartlett.

ranges, but *stimsoni stimsoni* was mapped as northern and western Western Australia, with *stimsoni orientalis* ranging from eastern Western Australia over the southern Northern Territory and South Australia to western and central Queensland and northwestern New South Wales.

There is little doubt that specimens from the eastern and western extremes of the range look quite distinctive, but over most of the area specimens can be rather randomly assigned to either subspecies. There is considerable variation with age as well as geography. It seems best to treat variation in this species as a cline, with a gradual west to east transition in counts and color characters. Most Australian workers do not appear to recognize the subspecies *A. s. orientalis*, and it here is treated as a synonym of *A. s. stimsoni*, leaving the species without formal subspecies.

There are indications in the literature that populations from the southeastern part of the range differ in build from typical specimens and that many areas may have localized color variants that will prove to be distinctive if studied further.

Natural History

The Blotched Python occurs in dry savannas, scrubland, and desert from coastal Western Australia to the Great Dividing Range in Queensland. Its range is bounded on the north by that of *A. childreni* and on the east by that of *A. maculosa*. It appears to hybridize with both these species where they come into contact. In Western Australia it encircles the range of the Anthill Python and may occur with it along the coast without hybridizing.

Like the other *Antaresia*, it is nocturnal. Specimens hide during the day in burrows, caves, crevices in the rocks, and under debris, emerging at night to feed on a variety of frogs, reptiles, and small mammals and birds. It appears to be an opportunistic feeder, utilizing any prey it can find in its rather desolate habitat. The area it lives in is mostly desert and very dry savanna or rocky areas.

Females seem to lay clutches of about six eggs during the Australian spring. Hatchlings are about 260 to 300mm long and feed on skinks and geckos. Adults will take small rodents and appear quite adaptable.

Husbandry

This common and variable python is virtually unstudied and apparently is not bred in captivity. It seldom is (legally)

This is a very nicely marked Blotched Python. This species is not common on the American market, and few are bred compared to Faded and Rough-spotted Pythons. Photo by K. H. Switak.

available to hobbyists but holds much promise if it ever should become available.

Taxonomic History

L. A. Smith described the species in his 1985 review of the group as *Liasis stimsoni stimsoni* from near Nullagine, Western Australia, and as *L. s. orientalis* from Winduldarra Rockhole, Western Australia. Both were described in *Rec. West. Aust. Mus.*, 9(3): 267-273.

It seems very likely that another review of *Antaresia* based on detailed examination of overlap areas of the species will show that all the forms except *A. perthensis* belong to a single variable species with subspecies. The oldest name for the group is *childreni*.

Genus *Aspidites* W. Peters, 1877 (*Monataber. Pruess. Akad. Wiss. Berlin*, 1876: 914). Type species by monotypy *melanocephalus* Krefft. *Aspidites* is a replacement name for *Aspidiotes* Krefft, preoccupied, and takes the same type species.

Synonyms: *Aspidiotes* Krefft, 1864.

Large, slender, narrowly ringed pythons with slender heads not much wider than the neck, the snout rounded to pointed. There are no premaxillary teeth and no thermosensory pits in the rostral, supralabial, or infralabial scales. The tail is moderately long (about 10 to 15% of total length) and the subcaudals are about half divided, half single. The eye is small and almost black.

Aspidites has a number of characteristics that are odd for pythons. One of the most obvious is their lack of labial pits. This is *Aspidites ramsayi*. Photo by C. Banks.

The two species are easily distinguished by coloration and counts: glossy black to blackish brown head and neck in *A. melanocephalus*, which commonly has more than 315 ventrals; brown to golden reddish brown head and paler neck in *A. ramsayi*, which commonly has fewer than 308 ventrals.

ASPIDITES MELANOCEPHALUS
Black-headed Python

This slender, colubrid-like python has a unique glossy black (to deep brownish black with reddish tints) hood covering the entire head and about 20 scales onto the neck. The snout is more rounded than in Ramsay's Python.

Description

Cylindrical, slender pythons with narrow heads not distinct or barely distinct from the neck. The snout is rounded, the rostral scale large and somewhat protuberant. From above, the rostral is pointed and partially divides the squarish internasals. There are two pairs of prefrontals, the anterior larger than the posterior and in broad contact, the posterior often broader than high and in narrow contact (occasionally separated by the anterior prefrontals). The frontal is rather triangular and may be followed by several often indistinct pairs of parietal scales. The supraoculars are large and seldom divided. From the side, the nostril is mostly lateral and the large nasal scale is separated from the two (rarely three) preoculars by one to three (rarely four) loreals. There are three or four postoculars and usually one or two suboculars, but often one

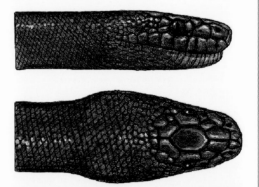

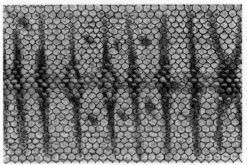

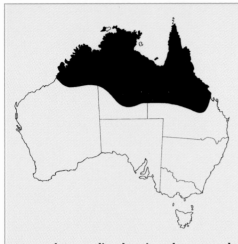

Map of Australia showing the natural range of A. *melanocephalus*.

or two supralabials enter the eye. There are 10 or 11 (sometimes 12) supralabials and 14 to 18 infralabials, none pitted.

The dorsal scales are in 50 to 65 rows at midbody, with a typical formula of 37-46 one head length behind the head, 50-60 at midbody, and 35-37 one head length before the vent. The ventral scales number 315-359, and there are 60 to 75 subcaudals, more than half of which are singles, especially anteriorly.

Males probe about 10 to 12 subcaudals.

This is a distinctively colored species with an obvious glossy blackish hood covering the entire head and the neck back for 20 or more scales; in young the hood extends downward to cover the anterior ventral scales. The body is sandy brown to yellowish or pale reddish tan and covered with many (often 80 to 100) rather irregular dark brown to dark reddish brown rings or broken

Head and midbody view of A. *melanocephalus*.

bands that are two to four scales wide. The bands often blend together on the midback to produce a mostly dark brown band or stripe. In other specimens the rings continue around the back. Some specimens give the appearance of oblique vertical bands on the sides somewhat separated from transverse bands over the back. There may be small brownish blotches between the major bands on the sides. The belly is whitish to pinkish with dark smudges and blotches.

Adults commonly are 1.5 to 2 meters in length, but there is a record of a specimen 3023mm long from Western Australia. A weight of 16 kilos is reported for a large captive adult.

Natural Variation

The color pattern varies considerably from individual to individual, with small specimens having the most distinct and uniform banding. Large, old specimens may be very pale with indistinct darker brown bars or oblique smudges. At the other extreme are specimens with the blackish color of the head extending posteriorly over most of the back as a broad dark brown band.

The population in western central Western Australia (Port Headland south to Yardie Creek) may be isolated from more northern and interior populations, but there may still be some gene exchange, and differences, if any, are weakly defined. The parietals in far-western specimens tend toward a single pair, while they usually form two or three distinct pairs in specimens from the rest of the range. Western Australian specimens may have fewer loreals (one versus two or three) and generally lack suboculars as compared to more eastern and northern specimens. No subspecific name has been proposed for the Port Headland, Western Australian population, and many more specimens will have to be studied to determine if it is distinctive and whether or not it is isolated.

A. melanocephalus is a wide-ranging snake that occurs in just about any habitat that can support its burrowing and reptile-eating habits. Photo by R. D. Bartlett.

A. ramsayi has the pointed snout and underslung jaw typical of burrowing snakes. Photo by I. Francais.

anterior ones long, the posterior ones smaller and often in limited contact above the anterior prefrontals. The frontal is rather triangular and separates the large undivided supraoculars. The parietal scales form a single indistinct pair usually separated by a distinct interparietal. From the side, the nostril is lateral in position and the nasal scale is separated from the two (rarely one or three) preoculars by two or rarely three loreals. There are three to six small postoculars. The supralabials form a series of 10 to 14 sometimes very irregular scales, usually with two supralabials entering the lower margin of the eye unless one or two small suboculars intervene. There are 14 to 19 infralabials.

The midbody dorsal scales are in 43 to 65 rows, with a typical formula of 32-42 scales one head length behind the head, 50-60 at midbody, and 33-51 one head

length before the vent. There are 273-315 ventrals and 43-55 subcaudals. Most of the subcaudals in this species are undivided, the divided ones coming toward the end of the tail.

In coloration Ramsay's Python is distinctive but similar to the Black-headed Python. The head and middle of the back are bright to dark reddish brown, the sides paler brown or sandy tan, usually with many narrow (three or four scales wide) vertical or oblique brownish bars. Adults vary from having uniform brownish bands over the sides and back to being almost uniformly pale reddish brown with traces of dark patches on the sides. Some specimens seem to have the bands in several rows and vaguely resemble the six rows of spots in carpet pythons. The belly is yellowish to cream with some dark spots and blotches.

Natural Variation

Juveniles have a dark, almost black, spot on the snout and a similar band over the head from eye to eye. Adults from most of the range lose this pattern with age, but those from New South Wales retain three dark spots, on the snout and over each eye. These spotted adults were named *collaris*, but the type of *ramsayi* also is a New South Wales specimen and both names seem to apply to the same type of variation, so *collaris* is a synonym. Specimens from southwestern Australia may be isolated from the rest of the species, but if so they differ in few regards, specifically somewhat lower ventral counts, the common lack of suboculars, and a tendency toward fewer midbody dorsal scales. Specimens from southwestern Australia have been described as both more distinctly banded than eastern specimens and as lacking distinct bands, so there probably is the same amount of color variation as in the rest of the range.

Hatchlings and juveniles have the most strongly patterned bodies and heads. In some juveniles the bars on the body are heavily fused and form more of a network than a regular series of bands. The belly may be uniformly brownish, becoming paler with age.

Males probe about 8 to 12 subcaudals.

Typical adults are about 1.5 meters long. The maximum length seems to be between 2.7 and 3 meters.

Ramsay's Python has a subdued but beautiful pattern. This and their rarity on the market make them highly coveted snakes. Photo by K. H. Switak.

Natural History

Ramsay's Python is widespread over the dry interior of Australia, occurring from Western Australia to northern New South Wales and southern Queensland. It reaches the coast only north of Port Headland, Western Australia, where the desert reaches the shore. It has been suggested that this range is broken into three populations of unequal size, one over the great central desert, one near the coast in northern Western Australia, and the other in interior southwestern Western Australia. However, these populations, if distinct, are little differentiated, and many herpetologists feel the range of the species is continuous.

Once a traditional food of Australian natives, Ramsay's Python is active mostly at night and feeds on a variety of small mammals and birds as well as lizards and snakes. It is not nearly as confirmed a reptile-eater as is the Black-headed Python. Its days are spent in burrows, some self-dug using the pointed snout, and under logs and other litter.

This python is able to survive both in dry savanna with sparse shrubs and spinifex grass as well as in virtually barren sandy areas.

Ramsay's Python may be quite common locally and often is conspicuous, but it is not well-known in nature. It lays its eggs in October and they hatch in December. The species, like other Australian fauna, is strictly protected.

Husbandry

Though Ramsay's Python remains uncommon and very expensive, it is seen in small numbers in captivity and now is being captive-bred in fair numbers. It needs a large terrarium because it is an active species, and it likes warm temperatures and warm basking areas. They feed fairly well on rodents and other mammals and birds and adjust well to captivity.

Mating may occur all year long, but fertile matings seem to be restricted to the winter months in the Northern Hemisphere. Females lay clutches of some 5 to 15 eggs and brood them in the usual coiled position. If removed to an incubator at about 32°C (90°F), they hatch in about 60 to 70 days. The young are about 440mm long and are brightly banded. They will accept rodents as well as lizards when a few weeks old. The pattern intensifies over the first months of life and then begins to get duller each year.

Though a relatively docile species, it is large enough and strong enough to require some care in handling. The legal status of this species in the North American and European hobbies may be questionable, as there is a great deal of smuggling involving this species and the Black-head. There is some evidence that the species is declining or perhaps almost extirpated in southwestern Australia.

Taxonomic History

It is hard to understand why this distinctive species was not recognized until just over a hundred years ago, but *Aspidiotes ramsayi* (note the use of the old spelling) was not described until 1882 by Macleay in *Proc. Linnean Soc. New South Wales*, 6: 813. The type locality is Fort Bourke, New South Wales. In 1913, Longman described *Aspidites collaris* from Avondale Station, near Cunnamulla, New South Wales (*Mem. Queensland Mus.*, 2: 40). This form appears to be the same as that described from a nearby area by Macleay, and it is considered a synonym. No other names presently are in the synonymy of this species.

Genus *Liasis* Gray, 1842 (*Zool. Misc.*: 44). Type species by subseq. design. *mackloti* Dumeril & Bibron. The type species was established by Opinion 1514 (*Bull. Zool. Nom.*, 45(3): 244, Sept. 1988).

Synonyms: *Bothrochilus* Fitzinger, 1843 [*boa*]; *Leiopython* Hubrecht, 1879 [*albertisi*]; *Lisalia* Gray, 1849 [*olivaceus*]; *Nardoa* Gray, 1842 (preocc.) [*boa*]; *Nardoana* Berg, 1901 (replc. *Nardoa*).

The Australian Water Python, *Liasis fuscus*, has head scalation details that are fairly typical for the genus. Photo by P. J. Stafford.

Moderately large, cylindrical pythons that usually are glossy dark brown to greenish brown above (occasionally with pale specks) or glossy blackish brown ringed with orange. The head has fully developed shields. There is one large loreal scale that rarely is fragmented as an individual variation. The rostral scale may have strong pits, weak pits, or no pits, and the supralabials usually have only the first scale with a strong sensory pit, sometimes two pitted, sometimes none pitted. The posterior infralabials have pits. Often the supralabials below the eye have a shallow depression at the edge of the eye. The tail is not prehensile, and the posterior dorsal scales bear two apical pits.

I tentatively recognize eight species of *Liasis* here, including two elevated from subspecific rank to specific level: *savuensis* and *barroni*. Both these taxa seem to be isolated geographically and have good distinctions from the closest relatives, and presently intergrades are not known.

KEY TO THE SPECIES OF LIASIS

A. Upper lip white, strongly barred with black; deep sensory pits in the rostral, supralabials, and infralabials................*albertisi*

AA. Upper lip dark to pale, never contrastingly barred black and white; sensory pits present or absent from rostral and supralabials, usually weak.........B

B. Lips dark, often almost black; pattern commonly of blackish rings against an orange to deep brown background; no rostral sensory pits.................*boa*

BB. Lips pale; pattern speckled or unicolored; usually with at least traces of rostral sensory pits...C

C. Color pattern of grayish to bluish brown background with numerous small pale and darker speckles and spots......................D

CC. Body glossy olive green to dark brown without pale specks..E

D. Dorsal scale rows at midbody 49 to 53; ventrals 270 to 280; upper labials 10 or 11; eye very pale, appearing relatively large...*savuensis*

DD. Dorsal scale rows at midbody 55 to 63; ventrals 292 to 304; upper labials 11 or 12; eye heavily reticulated with dark, appearing small...............*mackloti*

E. Upper portion of nasal scale produced backward, separating anterior prefrontal from loreal; dorsal scales in 63 to 72 rows at midbody; ventrals 358 to 374; olive brown above with black skin between scales..............*papuanus*

EE. Anterior prefrontal in contact with loreal, the nasal scale not separating them; skin between scales pale....................F

F. Dorsal scales at midbody in 40 to 55 rows; ventrals 271 to

---

Most of the species of *Liasis* come from humid environments and need to be kept accordingly. This is a Ringed Python, *L. boa*. Photo by R. Sprackland.

286; back with an oily blue-gray sheen, belly yellow and strongly contrasting to back............*fuscus*

FF. Dorsal scales at midbody in more than 55 rows; ventrals more than 300; back olive-green to brown, grading into yellowish white belly................................G

G. Midbody scale rows 61 to 72; ventrals 321 to 377; northern Australia...........................*olivaceus*

GG. Midbody scale rows 58 to 63; ventrals 374 to 411; Pilbara region, Western Australia......*barroni*

LIASIS ALBERTISI
White-lipped Python

The strongly black and white barred lips of this python are distinctive, and it could be confused only with *Python boeleni*, the Imperial Python, which has oblique yellow bars on the lower sides and the posterior belly black.

Description

The White-lipped Python is a slender, cylindrical python with thin skin and an extremely high iridescence. The tail is long (about 14 to 17% of the total length) and the head is narrow with a long snout. From above, the snout is somewhat squarish, the rostral narrowly visible. There are deep sensory pits in the rostral scale. The internasals are large and squarish and are followed by a pair of large, strap-like prefrontals in contact with the frontal. Occasionally a small pair of posterior prefrontals is present and contacts the frontal, being widely separated by the anterior prefrontals. The frontal is large

Map of New Guinea and eastern Indonesia showing the general distribution of *L. albertisi*.

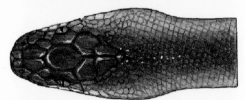

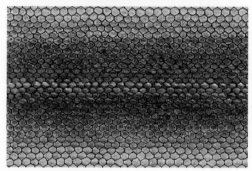

Head and midbody views of *L. albertisi*.

and oval and the supraoculars are large and single. Usually one pair of rather small parietals is present, but occasionally there is a second small pair separated by an interparietal scale. From the side, the large nasal scale is separated from the large single preocular (rarely with one to three very small lower preoculars) by a large trapezoidal loreal in wide contact with the anterior prefrontal. There are 12 to 14 supralabials, the first and second

apparently confirmed record of one 6.5 meters long. A specimen 3.7 meters long weighed over 9 kilos. Larger specimens are considerably more bulky.

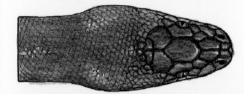

Map of Australia showing the general distribution of *L. barroni.*

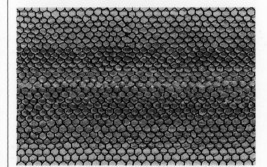

Head and midbody views of *L. barroni.*

Natural Variation

There is considerable variation in the number and sizes of the posterior prefrontals. The color shade also varies considerably from deep glossy brown to dull greenish.

Natural History

Virtually nothing is known of the natural history of this rare species. It typically is found near water, often on rocky soils, and is largely terrestrial. It seems to eat mostly mammals, with a good percentage of birds and reptiles probably entering the diet.

The range of this species is restricted to the dry, rocky Pilbara region of Western Australia, well to the south of the closest populations of *L. olivaceus.* There is every indication that the two species are isolated and no longer can share genes, and there are considerable differences between the two, especially in the lower number of midbody dorsal scale rows and the very high ventral count. There do not seem to be any obvious differences in color and pattern, but admittedly no one has ever compared many living specimens of the two species.

Husbandry

This species apparently is not in captivity and there are no records of it being maintained in the hobby or in zoos.

Taxonomic History

In 1981, L. A. Smith described this taxon as *Liasis olivaceus barroni (Rec. West. Aust. Mus.,*

The Pilbara Python is a rare and mysterious animal much in need of study to determine its habits and taxonomic relationships. Photo by K. H. Switak.

Map of New Guinea and the surrounding islands showing the approximate natural range of *L. boa.*

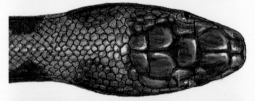

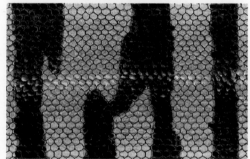

Head and midbody views of *L. boa.*

9(2): 231), with the type specimen coming from Tambrey, Western Australia. The restricted distribution and significant differences in scale counts are sufficient to grant this form the status of a full species. Also, as a full species it is likely to gain more attention from scientists and hobbyists.

LIASIS BOA
Ringed Python

The Ringed Python sometimes is called the Halloween Snake because most of its hatchlings are brilliant orange and black in color. Unfortunately this color does not last, and most adults are deep blackish brown with just faint orange-brown rings or irregular bands. Still, it is a small python that has proved easy to maintain, and it has quite a following.

Description

The head is rather long and ends in a squarish snout, the rostral scale barely visible from above. Unlike any other *Liasis,*

there are no pits on the rostral scale and none on the supralabials (other species lack pits on either the rostral or the supralabials but not both). From above, the internasals are large and squarish. They are followed by a pair of large anterior prefrontals (occasionally partially fused) that reach the frontal. The frontal is oval or squarish and separates the large, undivided supraoculars. The anterior parietals are large and distinct,

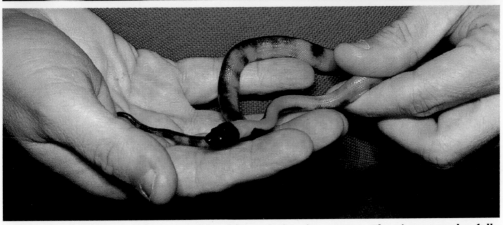

Young Ringed Pythons show considerable variation in pattern. The rings may be fully formed, restricted to spots along the sides, or reduced to muddy blotches. Notice that the head normally is solid black, regardless of the body pattern. Photos by M. Walls. Courtesy of Intelligent Propagations.

but the posterior prefrontals may be large or small and regular or irregular; commonly several small scales separate the parietals. From the side, the nasal scale is rather slender and elongated, and the loreal is small and squarish but in contact with the prefrontal. The single preocular is very large, and there are two or three large postoculars. There are 9 to 12 (usually 10 or 11) supralabials, two or three forming the lower margin of the orbit; no supralabials have sensory pits, but the fifth has a distinct oblique depression below the eye. There are about 12 or 13 infralabials, several of the posterior ones pitted.

The dorsal scales are large and in only 34 to 39 rows at midbody; there are 31 to 34 scale rows one head length behind the head and 25 to 27 one head length before the vent. The ventrals number 245 to 267, and there are 45 to 54 mostly divided subcaudals.

The hemipenes extend for 10 or 11 subcaudals and are forked, with a small awn (papilla) at the tip of each branch. The sulcus bifurcates low on the organ, well before the center. There are five flounces concentrated toward the distal half of the organ.

Coloration is relatively simple. Adults are a deep glossy blackish brown, either apparently unicolor or with traces of 12 or more broad olive brown bands or blotches on the sides. The paler blotches may be very irregular or may continue across the back as wide rings. The head is black above and over the lips, the throat brown to dark grayish. Often there is a trace of a pale spot behind the eye. The belly is yellowish, sometimes with large dark blotches at the sides. Hatchlings and young are very different in color, typically being

---

Typically, adult *L. boa* lose the attractive pattern of the juveniles and become muddy and dull in appearance. Photo by R. D. Bartlett.

This is a pair of adult *L. boa* that have retained quite a bit of the juvenile pattern. Selective breeding may one day lead to nicely marked adults. Photo by R. Kayne.

bright orange (sometimes duller and more brownish) from the nape to the tail tip with many (often 30 or more) broad black bands running from side to side over the back. (The black pattern in captive-bred specimens often is greatly reduced and may be restricted to oval blotches low on the sides, few or none extending to the midline of the back; other specimens have the black bands variously wide and narrow, complete or broken, apparently as an individual variation.) The head is glossy black from the nape to the snout, including the lips, and there is an elongated orange spot or short stripe behind the eye, sometimes with a smaller spot before the eye. The belly is bright yellow. The orange begins to dull before the snake is a year old. The eye is nearly black.

This is a small python, adults commonly a meter long. Few specimens reach 1.5 meters, but the record appears to be nearly 2 meters.

Natural Variation

Though the scalation is relatively constant in this species (which might be expected considering its small geographic range), the color pattern is exceedingly variable in regard to the development of the bands in young specimens. Typically the black bands are broad and quite symmetrical, the black and orange alternating in a regular fashion and crossing the back. Often the black bands are split with orange, producing two narrower bands or one broad and one very narrow band. In some specimens the black bands are offset at the midline of the back and produce a pattern of alternating squares when seen from above. In still others, the black often does not reach the midline of the back at all, being restricted to the side. Occasional specimens have the black confined to rather symmetrical ovals low on the sides, giving a spotted appearance rather than a banded one. A few young are hatched completely lacking black on the body; these become the unicolored adults occasionally reported. The orange begins to become infiltrated with melanin when the snakes are about three to six months old, and all the orange may be almost invisible by the age of one year. The orange spot behind the eye seldom is visible in adults.

Natural History

The Ringed Python is restricted to the Bismarck Archipelago, a group of rather large islands off the northeastern coast of New Guinea (and politically part of Papua New Guinea). The Bismarcks include New Britain, New Ireland, and Duke of York Island as well as much smaller islands. The terminal island group of the Bismarcks (including Massau Island) is occupied by *L. albertisi*, considered to be a very close relative of *L. boa*. Old records from the mainland of New Guinea appear to be misidentifications, as do records for the Celebes, Solomons, and Tokelau Islands.

Liasis boa is a terrestrial nocturnal species often found in very moist forests and swamps. It has been suggested that the brilliant colors of the hatchling are an attempt at mimicry of a local venomous snake, though no orange and black model appears to be mentioned in the literature. (The model suggested most often, *Pseudechis colletti*, is restricted to Queensland, Australia, and is out of the question unless Ringed Python predators read herpetology texts.) Little is reported on details of the natural history, but the species seems to be common and well-known to the natives. It would appear to feed on the usual mammals and birds supplemented with reptiles.

Few legal importations of Ringed Pythons reach the hobby, but the species is widely bred in captivity.

Husbandry

Because it is a relatively small and docile species (though well able to produce vicious bites), Ringed Pythons can be kept in small cages in the fashion normal for other pythons. They do well in a cage with a secure hide box, a water bowl, and a warm basking area. They seldom climb. Temperatures of about 30 to 32°C (86 to 90°F) are fine most of the year, with a nighttime drop to about 25 or 26°C (77 to 79°F). In the winter, breeding stock (at least three to four years old) can be subjected to the usual short day lengths and cooler temperatures of most python breeding programs. During the summer the snakes do well with 14 hours of light per day.

Females lay clutches of about 12 to 16 eggs that are creamy white in color and about 45mm long. Eggs incubated in vermiculite at 32°C (90°F) or a bit lower hatch in about 60 to 70 days. The young are some 300 to 320mm long. Some hatchlings feed on mice, but others may require lizards or forced feeding. Young that survive for a few months on lizards usually eventually begin feeding on mice.

There are conflicting reports as to the aggressiveness of this species to its own kind. When housed together, males may fight viciously, drawing blood, so it is best to house males separately. Combat between males before mating may be normal for the species but is not essential to successful egg-laying.

Additionally, females often have been accused of cannibalism, killing and eating other females and young housed with them. This probably is not normal but reflects some problem with the housing conditions. However, most small terrestrial pythons do feed on some reptiles in nature and it might be best to not take a chance with these expensive pythons.

Captive-bred young occasionally are available and sell for high prices. Though beautiful, this species should not be purchased because of the juvenile color, because this is just a passing thing. Though very glossy, the adults may appear very plain in coloration (i.e., all black) at first glance and may not be every hobbyist's cup of tea.

Ringed Pythons need a relatively high humidity to thrive in captivity. A hide box with some damp sphagnum moss in it will give your pet a nice, moist retreat. Photo by P. Freed.

Taxonomic History

The Ringed Python was described in 1837 by Schlegel as *Tortrix boa* (*Essai Phys. Serp.*, 2: 22) from New Ireland in the Bismarck Archipelago. The species has gathered no synonyms (except for the replacement name *schlegeli* proposed by Gray in *Zool. Misc.* in 1842 during one of his flights of abstruse taxonomic wisdom) but has been rather consistently referred to monotypic genera, including *Nardoa*, *Nardoana* (to replace the preoccupied *Nardoa*), and *Bothrochilus*. *Liasis boa* is very similar and closely related to *L. albertisi*, and the two seem to be replacement species derived from a common ancestor. Adults are very similar in coloration, with *L. boa* having lower scale counts than typical for the genus and *L. albertisi* having much more strongly developed sensory pits than typical for the genus.

LIASIS FUSCUS

Australian Water Python

This simply colored dark python is the Australian (and southeastern New Guinea) segment of a group of species that includes *L. albertisi*, *L. mackloti*, and *L. savuensis*. Morphologically the four species are quite similar, but they all have different ranges and are considered full species.

Description

The Australian Water Python is a cylindrical, rather slender python with a long, rounded snout and relatively slender head. The eye is very dark.

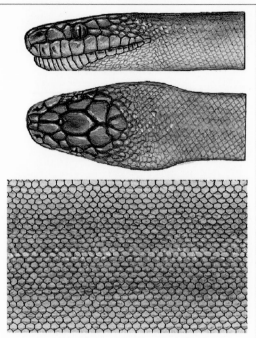

Head and midbody views of *L. fuscus*.

From above, the rostral is easily visible and may partially separate the rather elongated internasals. The rostral does not have sensory pits (rarely present but weak in New Guinea specimens). There is a pair of large anterior prefrontals in wide contact with the frontal in most specimens, as well as a small pair of posterior prefrontals that usually are separated by the anterior prefrontals. The frontal is large and oval, and there may be one or two pairs of parietals separated by interparietal scales. From the side, the nasal scale is large and slightly produced backward. The single loreal is large and rectangular, with a fairly wide contact with the anterior prefrontal. The single preocular is large, and there are two to four large postoculars. There are 11 or 12 supralabials, two forming the lower margin of the orbit; the first supralabial has a distinct pit, and the second sometimes is pitted. There are 15 to 17 infralabials, the posterior ones pitted.

The dorsal scales are in 45 to 48 rows at midbody, about 39 to 42 one head length behind the head, and 27 to 30 one head before the vent. The ventrals number 271 to 286, and there are 72 to 86 subcaudals, mostly paired. (These counts apply to specimens from Western Australia; counts from other literature are 40 to 55 midbody scale rows, 270 to 300 ventrals, and 60 to 90 subcaudals, but these may be confused in part with other *Liasis* at various times considered to be subspecies of *fuscus* or *mackloti*.)

The hemipenis is shallowly forked, each branch ending in a small awn (papilla). The sulcus is forked for over half the length of the organ. The male hemipene pouches probe 10 to 12 subcaudals.

Australian Water Pythons are uniformly dark brown (almost black) to greenish or bluish gray over the back, with the undersides white to yellowish, the tail sometimes dark below. The contrast between the dark sides and the belly is sharp. The lips are whitish, often much brighter behind the eye than in front of the eye. This is a very iridescent python, especially when freshly shed, and many specimens have an oily sheen.

Average adults are 1.5 to 2 meters in length, with a few specimens reaching 3 meters.

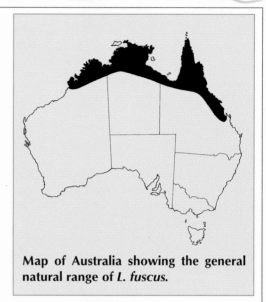

Map of Australia showing the general natural range of *L. fuscus*.

Natural Variation

Like most pythons, the head scales are quite variable in details, and the parietals are especially variable. Australian populations seem to show little organized variation, most details of scalation and color being individual variations.

Specimens from southeastern New Guinea are generally similar to Australian specimens, and there probably still is some gene flow through the islands in the Torres Strait. There may be fewer subcaudals, 67 to 76, than in Australian specimens, but if so the difference seems very small. New Guinea specimens may have shallow pits in the rostral scale lacking in Australian specimens. Supposedly all New Guinea specimens are black, lacking the brown tones often found in Australian specimens.

Natural History

Australian Water Pythons are found in low, often marshy areas

Despite the rather plain colors, *L. fuscus* frequently show a very pretty iridescent sheen on their scales. Photo by R. D. Bartlett.

along the northern coast of Australia from northern Western Australia to the central Queensland coast, plus islands in the Torres Strait and the adjacent area of southeastern New Guinea. During the wet season this is an almost aquatic snake, feeding in the water and retreating to water when threatened. It seldom is found far from water at any season of the year. It also is very adaptable to man and has a reputation for raiding hen houses and eating chickens. Its more natural menu consists mostly of mammals and water birds, with some reptiles taken as well.

Males are aggressive and often fight before mating. Reproduction in nature may be timed to produce young at the beginning of the rainy season when there is a greater number of prey species available. In such cases the eggs may be laid in July and August to hatch in November and December. Females brood their eggs in mammal burrows or in depressions near the edges of lakes and rivers.

Husbandry

Though they are hardy and can be very colorful when freshly molted, Australian Water Pythons are not especially popular in captivity. They often are very aggressive, being quick to strike, and males cannot be caged together without risking bloody fights. Hatchlings also may be very aggressive.

As you would expect, the snakes should be given a roomy terrarium with a large box of moist sphagnum. Provide a warm basking area and access to a large water bowl. Many specimens seem to do best if given a large temperature drop at night (but be sure there is a warm basking area available). Most *L. fuscus* will take mammals and birds in captivity.

Breeding in captivity may occur without any obvious incentives or may be induced by a cool period. Females lay clutches of about six to 20 eggs that are 60mm long. They can be incubated in moist vermiculite at the usual 32°C (90°F). Incubation takes about 60 days. The hatchlings are over

Liasis cornwallisius Guenther, 1879 (*Ann. Mag. Nat. Hist.*, (5) 3: 85) from Cornwallis Island in the Torres Strait and *Nardoa crassa* Macleay, 1885 (*Proc. Linn. Soc. New South Wales*, 10: 66) from the Herbert River District of Queensland are this species. Unfortunately *L. fuscus* has suffered from the tendency of many taxonomists to make

Australian Water Pythons are generally aggressive snakes that are quite a challenge to handle. Always be on guard when working with this species. Photo by R. D. Bartlett.

400mm long, often shed and begin to feed in less than a week, and grow quickly. Maturity often is reached by three years of age.

Taxonomic History

Wilhelm Peters first described *Liasis fuscus* from Port Bowen (now Port Clinton), Queensland, in 1873 (*Monataber. Pruess. Akad. Wiss. Berlin*, 1873: 607).

guesses as to relationships of species and then combine many names as subspecies of a single diverse species. At various times *fuscus* has been considered a subspecies of *mackloti* and also to have *albertisi* as a subspecies. *L. albertisi* and *L. fuscus* may occur together in southeastern New Guinea and show no signs of intergrading. *L. mackloti* proper seems to be an island species with a very different color pattern and details of scalation, and there is no proof that it makes any morphological or geographical approach to *L. fuscus*.

LIASIS MACKLOTI
Island Water Python

The Island Water Python remains one of the most poorly known species of *Liasis*, and it so far has not been studied in detail. Few specimens enter the market or are preserved in collections. My concept of this species follows the redescription by Brongersma (1956a), except that I treat his subspecies *savuensis* as a full species.

Map of Indonesia showing the general distribution of *L. mackloti*.

Description

L. mackloti is a rather slender terrestrial python with a long tail (about 15% of total length) and a rather narrow head. From above the snout is rather squared off, the rostral barely visible. The rostral scale may have shallow pits or no pits. The nasals are separated by rectangular internasals. The anterior prefrontals are long and rather oval and usually contact the frontal, though there may be a small scale preventing their full contact. There is a pair of small squarish posterior prefrontals to the side of the anterior prefrontals and not in contact with each other. The frontal is large and oval to squarish; the supraoculars are large and single. Typically there is a distinct pair of large parietals behind the frontal and a smaller secondary pair separated from the first by several small and irregular scales. From the side, the large nasal is separated from the large single preocular by a squarish loreal that is in contact with the anterior prefrontal; rarely there are two loreals on one or both sides. There are two postoculars. There are 11 or 12 supralabials, the first two (rarely three) with shallow sensory pits. Two supralabials touch the eye below. There are 17 to 19 infralabials, the posterior ones weakly pitted.

The dorsal scales are in 55 to 65 rows at midbody; the rows one head length behind the head number 48 to 51, and those one head length before the vent 31 to 35. There are 292 to 304 ventrals and 86 to 96 mostly paired subcaudals.

The overall appearance is that of a dark python with pale mottling. The middle of the back tends to be more uniformly grayish brown to blue-gray than the paler sides. The top of the head is dark and often heavily mottled with darker brown, while the body is covered with a very irregular network of groups of pale grayish scales and darker brownish scales, the pale scales often forming indistinct lozenges or blotches on the sides. The belly

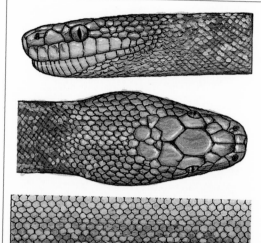

Head and midbody views of *L. mackloti.*

and there is considerable variation in the structure and number of parietals. The presence of two loreals in a few specimens is unusual in this genus but has been recorded in at least two specimens. As in most snakes with mottled patterns, no two specimens are exactly alike.

Natural History

Liasis mackloti in the restricted sense is known only from Timor and adjacent Samao Island plus Wetar Island, to the east of the Savu Sea in the Flores of eastern Indonesia. Little has been reported of their natural history, but it can be assumed that they occur in most habitats on these low islands and eat mammals and birds and perhaps reptiles. The days are hot and humid, with sizable temperature drops at night.

is yellow, extending onto the side for about a scale row and also extending onto the upper lips. Posteriorly the belly becomes heavily covered with brownish blotches until it is largely dark under the tail. The eye is dark brown to paler grayish with an orange cast.

Adults reach about 1.5 to 2 meters in length.

Natural Variation

Too few specimens have been described in detail to be sure of the limits of variation. It once was thought that specimens from Wetar, north of Timor, had more dorsal scale rows at midbody than Timor specimens, but this does not appear to be the case. Pitting of the rostral scale varies from totally absent to weakly present,

L. mackloti, usually under the name Macklot's Python, is beginning to show up more frequently on breeder lists, but it is still nowhere near common. Photo by I. Francais.

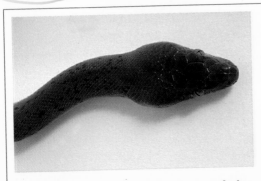

L. mackloti has a very restricted range, being known only from a few Indonesian islands. Photo by I. Francais.

Husbandry

Only a few typical *L. mackloti* are kept in captivity, though many related *L. savuensis* are now in the hands of hobbyists. They are aggressive snakes that are subject to respiratory infections and are not very colorful, so they are unlikely to ever become popular.

They can be housed like most pythons of similar size. Males may fight, so it is best to keep them separated. Breeding has been spurred by giving the animals both a cool period for a month or two and by providing large differences between daytime high temperatures and low nighttime temperatures. The animals like a temperature of 32°C (90°F) during the day with a warmer basking spot, dropping to 21°C (70°F) for at least a few hours at night. Mating occurs at night, as usual.

The females lay clutches of 8 to 14 eggs that they brood in the usual python fashion with occasional shivering. If the eggs are removed to an incubator set at 32°C (90°F), they hatch in

about 60 days. The eggs tend to be laid between April and June and hatch between June and August. Hatchlings are dark brown with few off-colored scales and dark eyes. The pale areas and darker scales develop with growth, and the eyes also lighten a bit. Hatchlings are aggressive but may not feed and often require force-feeding if they are to accept mice and not lizards. They mature in about three years.

Taxonomic History

Though *Liasis mackloti* was described by Dumeril and Bibron in 1844 (*Erpetol. Gen.*, 6: 440) from Timor, this species actually had been described earlier in the year by Mueller in a footnote to a report on a trip to Timor. Mueller called the snake *Python timorensis* and compared it to *P. amethistinus*. His *timorensis* (later modified to *timoriensis*) is not the same snake later described as *Liasis amethystinus* var. *timoriensis* by Peters in 1876 (now *Python timoriensis*). To recognize Mueller's name would force a new name on *mackloti* and also require that *Python timoriensis* (Peters) be renamed. Since the situation was noted by Brongersma, Mueller's name has been disregarded and officially abandoned to stabilize usage.

L. mackloti in the restricted sense has acquired one synonym, *dunni* Stull, 1932 (*Occas. Papers Boston Soc. Nat. Hist.*, No. 8: 25), described from Wetar Island. Stull thought that her specimens had more middorsal scale rows (61 to 63) than Timor and Samao

the neck. From above, the snout is broadly rounded and the rostral scale is barely visible. The rostral bears a pair of deep sensory pits. The nasal scales are separated by large, squarish internasals. The anterior prefrontals are large and usually reach the frontal; occasionally there is a pair of small posterior prefrontals lateral to the anterior prefrontals and in contact with the frontal. The frontal is large and more or less oval, and the supraoculars are large. There is a pair of large parietal scales behind the frontal. From the side, the nasal scale is very large and continued back along its upper margin, separating or nearly separating the single squarish loreal from the anterior prefrontal. There is a large preocular and sometimes a small lower preocular. There are two or three elongated postoculars. The supralabials number 10 or 11, the first and sometimes second with sensory pits. Two or three supralabials enter the lower margin of the eye and do not carry a shallow oblique depression. There are 16 to 20 infralabials, the posterior ones pitted.

The dorsal scales are in 63 to 72 rows at midbody; the scale

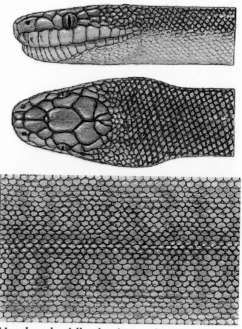

Head and midbody views of *L. papuanus*.

formula commonly includes 44 to 50 scale rows one head length behind the head and 30 to 32 rows one head length before the vent. There are 358 to 374 ventrals and 82 to 88 subcaudals (mostly paired).

The hemipenes are deeply forked and bear a large awn (papilla) at the tip of each branch. The sulcus is forked before the center of the organ. In males the hemipenes probe 10 to 12 subcaudals.

The Papuan Python is olive-brown to greenish above, paler and more grayish green on the sides, grading into the white belly. The lips may be pale, and there may be traces of a dark band back from the eye to the angle of the jaws. The skin between the scales of the head and body is black, and there may be faint black lines along the lip scales.

Map of New Guinea showing the general range of *L. papuanus*.

It is typical for Papuan Pythons to have dark skin between the scales, as this individual does. Photo by R. D. Bartlett.

The roof and floor of the mouth and the lining of the cloaca also are black. The black between the scales and in the mouth helps distinguish this species from the Olive Python, which is pale in these areas.

Adults are about 2 meters long on average, with a record of 4.4 meters; it probably grows longer.

Natural Variation

There is little literature on the Papuan Python, and it is poorly known. The simple color pattern permits little variation, and the head scalation appears quite constant. The occurrence of a lower preocular is uncommon in this species and has led to some taxonomic confusion.

Natural History

The Papuan Python is widely distributed over all of New Guinea from one tip of the island to the other, including at least some islands in Geelvink Bay. It seems to prefer low-lying areas that are very moist and is active at night. It feeds on mammals and birds in nature and has a reputation for being a snake-eater in captivity.

Husbandry

Papuan Pythons seldom are available and have been kept by few hobbyists or zoos. They have gained a reputation as very aggressive snakes that fight each other and are likely to become cannibalistic if placed in the same terrarium even for mating. They live for at least 20 to 30 years in captivity.

This species lays large eggs much like those of the Olive Python. An incubation period of about 90 days at 32°C (90°F) seems long, and perhaps a higher temperature would be better. Hatchlings feed on rodents.

Taxonomic History

First described by W. Peters and Doria in 1878 (*Annal. Mus.*

Civ. Stor. Nat. Giacomo Doria, Genova, 13: 400) from Bamoi in southwestern New Guinea, the species was poorly understood until redescribed by Brongersma in 1953 and 1956b. Traditionally it was listed as a subspecies of *Liasis olivaceus*, but McDowell in 1975 elevated it to full specific rank. *Liasis tornieri* Werner, 1897 (*Zool. Anz.*, 20: 261) from Stephansort (Bogadjim), New Guinea, represents a specimen with two preoculars. *Liasis maximus* Werner, 1936 (*Ann. Hist. Nat. Mus. Natl. Hungarici*, 30: 105) was described from a dried and possibly damaged skin probably from Astrolabe Bay, New Guinea. Several of the characters reported in the original description may be due to misinterpretations or damage, but generally the specimen agrees

---

Papuan Pythons should always be housed singly, for they are known to eat other snakes. Photo by V. Jirousek.

with *L. papuanus* except for lacking pits in the rostral and supralabials and having 55 rows of scales at midbody. If it comes from New Guinea it probably represents *L. papuanus*, but it cannot be confidently placed until a second specimen is taken and an accurate locality can be determined.

LIASIS SAVUENSIS
White-eyed Water Python

Originally described as a subspecies of *Liasis mackloti*, I can find no reason to consider this taxon a subspecies, so here I treat it as a full species because it is geographically isolated and quite distinctive in structure as well as color. Though there is no doubt that it is related to the Island Water Python, I feel it deserves full specific rank. The hobbyist literature on this form is only some two or three years old, and I feel that a change in common name to the more appropriate White-eyed Water Python is an improvement over the Savu or Sawu Island Python.

Description

The White-eyed Water Python is a small, cylindrical python with a speckled pattern and striking white eyes in adults. In general structure is it very similar to *L. mackloti*, but it differs in several counts. It is the most western form of the genus *Liasis* so far known.

The head is rather flattened, the snout squarish, and the head is distinct from the neck. From above, the rostral scale (without sensory pits) is barely visible and the nasals are separated by rectangular internasals in full contact with rather strap-like anterior prefrontals that usually are in contact with the frontal (occasionally a small scale comes between them and the frontal).

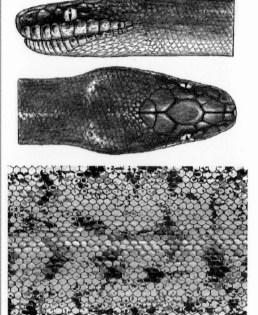

Map of Indonesia showing the natural range of *L. savuensis*

Head and midbody views of *L. savuensis.*

The posterior prefrontals are squarish and widely separated by the anterior prefrontals; they often fuse with the large preocular. The frontal is squarish to oval and is flanked by large, undivided supraoculars. There is a pair of large, obvious parietals after the frontal and then a band of irregular small scales preceding a barely distinct pair or group of slightly enlarged parietals. From the side, the large nasal scale is followed by a trapezoidal to rectangular loreal in contact with the anterior prefrontal. Often there is a second large loreal formed by fragmentation of the posterior lower corner of the main loreal. The preocular is large and single, and there are two large postoculars. The supralabials number 10 to 12 (average 10.5 in a small series), with two in contact with the lower margin of the eye. The first supralabial has a shallow pit, as may the second. There are 14 to 17 infralabials, the posterior ones pitted.

In Brongersma's original sample of five specimens, the scales at midbody were in 49 to 53 rows; there were 43 to 45 rows one head length behind the head and 29 to 31 one head length before the vent. There were 270 to 280 ventrals and 74 to 79 mostly paired subcaudals. In *L. mackloti* there are 55 to 65 scale rows at midbody, 292 to 304 ventrals, and 86 to 96 subcaudals (based on Brongersma's sample of five specimens plus the literature). No overlap in counts is reported for the two taxa.

In color *savuensis* is a speckled python that is mostly dark with orangish tan tones. The color (and pattern) change considerably over the life of the animal. Hatchlings are uniformly bright brick red or rusty brown with pale upper lips, white bellies, and pale golden orange eyes. With growth melanin appears to be deposited in many scales, especially anteriorly, so most adults appear dark brown on the head and a medium brown on the body, with large areas and individual scales paler brown to reddish brown. On the lower sides the pale areas become more distinctly orange. The belly remains white, though there may be rather large dark blotches at its edges. The lips of adults are mottled dull cream and brown, the white of the throat usually extending well onto the sides of the neck. Eye color gradually becomes less brown, until adults have striking white eyes with cleanly defined black pupils. The white eyes give the impression of being larger than in *mackloti*, but this probably is an illusion. Very old adults may be largely dark brownish black with just a few paler brown or orange-brown scales on the tail. The posterior part of the belly apparently does not become dark as in *mackloti*. Specimens often have a good bit of iridescence over the head, but this is not an exceptionally glossy python.

Average adults are small, perhaps averaging 700 to 900mm in total length. The maximum size is at least 1.3 meters, and the possibility exists that the species reaches 2 meters. Though often

Juvenile White-eyed Pythons frequently are reddish in color. They will change to the adult color gradually over the first year or so of their lives. Photo by M. Walls. Courtesy of Gary Lorio.

considered a dwarf python, adults are not much smaller than average adults of *L. mackloti*.

Natural Variation

There is the usual variation in details of head scalation to be expected in any python. The common presence of two loreals strongly relates this species to *Liasis mackloti*, as does the rest of the head scalation. The color change from a uniformly colored hatchling to a speckled adult also is as in *L. mackloti*, though *mackloti* are dark brown at hatching and become paler with age. The paling of the eye is found in other pythons but not so accentuated.

Because so few *L. savuensis* actually have been counted and measured, it should be expected

The staring, white eyes are the hallmarks of *L. savuensis.* Photo by R. D. Bartlett.

that the range of counts will be somewhat wider than found by Brongersma. However, this is a very isolated form with a small gene pool, and it may prove to be unexpectedly uniform in its counts.

Natural History

Liasis savuensis is, as far as known, confined to Sawu (Savu) Island at the western edge of the Savu Sea west of Timor. Presently the small island is heavily populated and there is little left of its original ecology. Whether *savuensis* occurs on neighboring islets in the Flores area is unknown, but these islands long have been inhabited by man, and the presence of a python might not have survived dogs, pigs, and chickens. The island is low and heavily vegetated, and the White-eye is said to be found over the entire island. It feeds on the available mammals and birds and probably reptiles as well. Sawu is a typical hot, humid Indonesian island with seasonally cooler nighttime temperatures.

Presently, and since 1993, the White-eyed Water Python is being imported in very large numbers. Considering its entire known range is only some 37 by 16 kilometers (smaller according to some reports) with a total area of 414 sq. kilometers (i.e., 23 by 10 miles, 160 sq. miles) and is heavily disturbed and populated, do not expect importations to continue much longer before the species is extinct in nature. Additionally, females produce small clutches of four or five eggs, and there must be a tremendous loss of young to dogs and pigs. The White-eyed Water Python has all the makings of a truly endangered species.

Husbandry

Since the large importations of White-eyes began, more and more python breeders have been trying their hand with this species. They have the advantages of being relatively gentle, most specimens not striking once they are acclimated, hardy, and small enough to house like a colubrid snake. Keepers often maintain their snakes in racks of plastic boxes much as they would a breeding group of kingsnakes or rat snakes. An adult is comfortable in a terrarium 300mm long, and since they are not climbers the cage does not have to be deep. Adults and most young feed readily on frozen and thawed mice and other rodents. They are happy at a temperature of 30 to 32°C (86 to 90°F) with somewhat lower temperatures at night and during the winter.

So far breeding has happened mostly in August and September, which probably is the natural season on Sawu. With continued breeding in captivity, breeders probably eventually will move the mating to the Northern Hemisphere winter or early spring as in most captive pythons. Females lay clutches of about four nearly round eggs about 50mm long some six weeks after mating. Incubation at about 30°C (86°F) and a bit higher lasts 60 to 70 days. The brick red hatchlings are about 320mm long and take mice after their first shed. Many do not feed voluntarily and may have to be force-fed. The mortality rate of eggs and hatchlings still is high.

At the moment, the average hobbyist is most likely to have access to wild-caught adults of the White-eyed Water Python, though there are several breeding programs doing rather well in the United States and Europe. Captive-breds still are largely being used by their breeders to increase colony size, so rather few captive-bred White-eyes are reaching the general terrarium market. This should change in a few years, and hopefully this pleasant little python with the staring eyes will become common in the hobby. Certainly it has no real future on its home island.

Taxonomic History

Brongersma described *Liasis mackloti savuensis* on the basis of five specimens in 1956 (*Proc. Konink. Nederl. Akad. Wetensch. Amsterdam,* (C) 59: 296-297). Curiously, his entire type series was collected in 1896 by Everett for the British Museum, and the first newly collected specimens may not have been taken until the 1980's. This is the first time the name *savuensis* has been used at the species level.

Successful breeding of White-eyed Pythons is becoming more commonplace. Therefore, this species is becoming more available and less expensive. Photo by R. D. Bartlett

Integrades between Diamond and Carpet Pythons, *P. spilotus spilotus* x *P. s. variegatus*, are beginning to be commonly available pythons. Photo by R. D. Bartlett.

diagonal slits and the infralabial pits are deep and placed in a groove; the hemipenis has three or more chevron-like flounces that point toward the base; and typically there is no dark spot below the eye. The character of the spot below the eye seems to me to be meaningless and certainly is too variable to include in a species group definition, but the character of the labial pits appears to be a strong one that holds up well. The *reticulatus* group basically is *Morelia* plus *Python reticulatus*, the species from the eastern part of the range of *Python*.

Most of the *molurus* group of pythons have a dark stripe through the eye, seen here on a Blood Python, *P. curtus*. Photo by P. J. Stafford.

IDENTIFICATION SUMMARY

I. *Molurus* group (supralabials with squarish pits, infralabials with weak pits not in a groove)

A. Head shields distinct

curtus—head dark above with narrow central line; dorsal scales 53-57; subcaudals 28-32

molurus—head with open arrowhead above; dorsal scales 61-75; subcaudals 58-73

sebae—head brown above with yellow stripes on sides; dorsal scales 76-98; subcaudals 62-76

AA. Head scales mostly small, shields behind prefrontals fragmented

anchietae—back mostly brown with yellow blotches; subcaudals 46-47

natalensis—back with large brown saddles; subcaudals 63-84

regius—back with a dark middorsal stripe and lateral bars; subcaudals 28-37

II. *Reticulatus* group (supralabials with oblique pits;

infralabials with deep pits posteriorly in a groove)

B. Head shields distinct

amethistinus—head plain or with transverse lines; 2 or 3 pairs parietals; dorsal scales 41-57; ventrals 289-346; subcaudals 85-120

boeleni—head black above, lips barred with yellow; 2 irregular pairs parietals; dorsal scales 44-51; ventrals 282-298; subcaudals 57-64+

oenpelliensis—head plain or weakly blotched; parietals fragmented; dorsal scales 70; ventrals 429-445; subcaudals 155-163

reticulatus—head with narrow vertical line from nape to snout; parietals fragmented; dorsal scales 69-79; ventrals 297-330; subcaudals 78-102

timoriensis—head with narrow vertical line from nape to frontal; 2 or 3 pairs parietals; dorsal scales 60-63; ventrals 287-289; subcaudals ?

BB. Head scales mostly small, shields behind prefrontals fragmented

The Green Tree Python, *P. viridis*, is now believed to be closely related to the Carpet Python and not deserving of its own genus. Photo by K. H. Switak.

bredli—8-12 scales between eyes; Northern Territory; ventrals 280-310; subcaudals 80-120

carinatus—body scales keeled; northwestern Australia; ventrals 298; subcaudals 83

imbricatus—3-6 scales between eyes; southwestern Australia; ventrals 239-276; subcaudals 63-82

spilotus—3-6 scales between eyes; eastern Australia and New Guinea; ventrals 251-310; subcaudals 63-94

viridis—adults bright green; ventrals 219-254; subcaudals 68-129

PYTHON AMETHISTINUS
Scrub Python

The Scrub or Amethystine Python is the largest python of the New Guinea—Australia area and

Map of New Guinea and surrounding islands showing the general distribution of *P. amethistinus*.

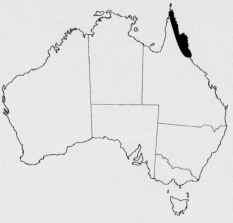

Map of Australia showing the general distribution of *P. amethistinus*

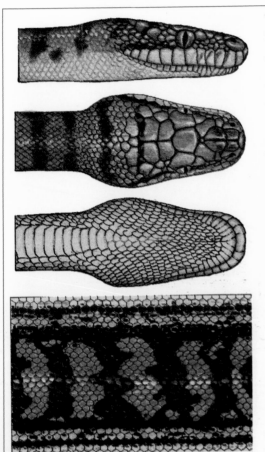

Head and midbody views of *P. amethistinus.*

is one of the most variable in color pattern. Unlike many other species of *Python*, it has a full set of well-defined head shields, though there are many small loreal scales. It is considered by some workers to be closely related to *Python reticulatus*, *P. timoriensis* serving as a connecting link between the two species, which are sympatric on a few small islands in eastern Indonesia.

Description

A long, slender, often compressed species with a long tail (almost 18% of total length).

The head is flattened and distinct from the neck. The eyes are dull golden.

From above, the head appears relatively narrow (especially in males) with a long, rounded to rather conical snout, the rostral scale visible and with two pits. The nasals are separated by a pair of squarish internasals. There are two pairs of prefrontals, the anterior pair much longer than the posterior pair and usually narrowly in contact with the frontal. The posterior prefrontals may be mostly lateral to the anterior prefrontals but still in contact with the frontal or in full contact with the frontal and separating the anterior prefrontals from making contact with the frontal. The frontal is large and oval or octagonal. The supraoculars are large, and there are three (sometimes two) pairs of large, symmetrical parietals. From the side, the nasal is followed by a variable number of loreals, typically 4 to 11 (sometimes 20 or so), of mixed sizes from large, distinct scales to tiny granules. There are two or three preoculars, the upper one very large and the lower one tiny, and four or five

The two black bands across the nape are characteristic of *P. amethistinus*. Photo by R. D. Bartlett.

This lightly colored Scrub Python would be considered a Class A specimen according to the traditional classification of this species. Photo by R. D. Bartlett.

postoculars. The supralabials number 11 to 14, the first four (sometimes five) with deep oblique pits. Two, rarely three, supralabials enter the eye. There are 17 to 24 infralabials, the anterior ones narrow and strap-like, the posterior ones small, six to eight posterior ones deeply pitted (and sometimes with a shallowly pitted anterior infralabial also). The pitted infralabials are sunken into a deep groove as in *P. reticulatus* and other southern *Python.*

There are typically 41 to 57 scales at midbody (with records as low as 39 in some Bismarck Archipelago specimens). The other body scale counts range from 34 to 45 one head length behind the head and 20 to 26 one head length in front of the vent. There are 289 to 346 ventrals, the lower number in the westernmost islands of the range, the highest in Queensland. The subcaudals are mostly paired and number 85 to 120, showing some random geographic variation.

The hemipenes are long (males probe to 14 subcaudals), forked, with a distinct apical awn on each branch. The sulcus bifurcates a bit beyond the middle of the organ. There are about six flounces, three on the stem.

Coloration is quite variable, but if correlated with geography the variation is too complex to be understood without extensive studies. Traditionally three types of color patterns are recognized, following Boulenger's classification of 1893. Class A specimens are uniformly golden to reddish brown with at best only traces of a darker pattern. Class B specimens are pale brown with broken or complete dark brown X marks over the back and two stripes, one pale, one dark brown, on the sides. Class C specimens are dark brown with irregular pale spots or cross-bars. Queensland, Australia, specimens fall into Class B and show little variation, while most more northern localities seem to have two pattern classes present. Over the entire range, uniformly colored specimens are less common than those with distinct to broken Xs on the back. The scales are iridescent. The head may be

This is one of the giant pythons, with typical adults about 2.5 to 4 meters long and many records of specimens exceeding 6 meters. The record may be a specimen 8.6 meters (28 feet) long.

Natural Variation

Though this species varies tremendously in color pattern, scale counts, and even head scalation, currently no subspecies are recognized. McDowell (1975) gave a brief analysis of variation in ventral counts and color

Adult Scrub Pythons are large and dangerous animals. Strict safety precautions must be observed when keeping this animal, and a keeper should never handle one without someone nearby. Photo by R. D. Bartlett.

uniformly brown similar to the body or there may be a narrow dark stripe back from each eye and two or three narrow lines across the back of the head; there may be smudges over the snout as well. The lip scales are mostly yellowish, as is the belly, but some island specimens have weak black barring on the upper lip scales.

patterns and concluded that some of the variation is clinal (a gradual change in a character with geography), counts increasing from west to east, and the color pattern variation does not seem to be strongly correlated with geography. Curiously, all the Queensland, Australia, specimens are Class B, with obvious Xs on the back and stripes on the side.

The Queensland form was described as *Liasis amethistinus kinghorni* by Stull in 1933 (dorsal scales 39/43-51/55-23/25; ventrals 328-344; subcaudals 108-116; one or more scales present between the parietals), but most authors today do not recognize this subspecies. It might be pointed out that absence of pattern classes is a type of differentiation, but it is not at all sure that the Australian snakes are isolated from those of New Guinea because the species is present on islands in Torres Strait. Of course, it is quite possible that several species are hidden in the concept of *P. amethistinus* and they will only surface when the species is studied in detail, including its biochemistry.

There is considerable variation with age, young specimens often being darker and duller than adults. The dark pattern may not develop for several months in some populations, hatchlings being uniformly reddish brown. Also, females may have broader snouts than males. This seems to be the most variable of the pythons at every level, but as usual, because of their size there are few adults preserved in collections.

Natural History

The Scrub Python is found from the islands of the Moluccas and Timor area (Ambon, Ceram, etc.) east over all the New Guinea area and adjacent islands southward into northeastern Queensland, Australia, as far south as Townsville. Over this large and varied range it occurs in dense rain forest, open dry forest, and coastal scrub areas. They prefer the vicinity of water and are at home both on land and in the trees and also swimming well. Obviously these are very adaptable snakes. Scrub Pythons feed on mammals of all types, from bats to wild pigs.

Males commonly fight before mating and may cause serious damage to competitors. Scrub Pythons are vicious biters and can strike for about half their body length. They react rapidly to the presence of prey or the keeper, and they have the reputation of striking at a keeper's face the moment the cage door is opened. This has for some reason limited their popularity among casual hobbyists.

Females produce about a dozen large (80 X 50mm), adhesive eggs that are laid mostly in the southern summer (August to December) in Australia and probably at any time of the year in New Guinea and the Indonesian islands. Females brood their eggs, shivering to produce a higher temperature. Incubation takes about 70 to 100 days, the hatchlings being 650 to 700mm long.

Scrub Pythons appear to be uncommon to rare snakes over much of their range, and they are respected where they occur because of their size and fearsome bite. They are protected in Australia and Papua New Guinea, but a few specimens are collected for the terrarium hobby in

Indonesian Irian Jaya and on some islands.

Husbandry

Like any large and aggressive snake, the hobbyist should consider all good and bad points of the snake before buying a specimen. Relatively few captive-breds are available, most specimens still being wild-caught imports that may be heavily parasitized and difficult to adjust to captivity. There is no down-playing the serious damage this species can inflict if it bites you, though occasional specimens (especially old, complacent adults) are relatively gentle, as are very young hatchlings. Adults are difficult to house, and young specimens grow rapidly.

If you decide on a Scrub Python, give it a very large and secure cage with sturdy climbing branches and a large water bowl. Temperatures between 26 and 32°C (79 to 90°F) are adequate, dropping as much as ten degrees at night. A basking area may be used because the snakes sometimes are active during the day.

Depending on origin of the specimens, a cool over-wintering period may be desirable to induce breeding; this would apply mostly to specimens from Queensland. Mating is accentuated if two males are present in a colony and allowed to fight, but such a setup may be not only too large for the typical hobbyist to maintain but also dangerous for the snakes. Females lay about a dozen eggs (5 to 21) that they will brood if given the chance. Most breeders remove the eggs at the first opportunity and incubate them in vermiculite at about 32°C (90°F). They hatch

Even large Scrub Pythons climb readily. You should include strong, securely anchored climbing branches in a Scrub Python enclosure. Photo by C. Banks.

in about 70 to 80 days in captivity. The young are almost uniform brown, becoming reddish brown after the first molt and then slowly gaining the adult dark pattern. The first shed takes place about two weeks after hatching, and the young then may take their first mice. Some young may not feed until two months old, living off of yolk remaining from the egg.

This is an uncommon snake in American and European terraria. So far it has not been bred often enough to develop constant color variations.

Taxonomic History

The Scrub Python has a long taxonomic history and has gathered a great number of synonyms. First described by Schneider in 1801 (*Hist. Amph.*, 2: 254) from an unknown locality, the type usually is assumed to have come from the Moluccas or some other Indonesian locality. The spelling of the specific name originally was *amethistina*, the later spelling *amethystina* being an unnecessary emendation. Other early synonyms include *jakati* Meyer, 1874 (New Guinea); *duceboracensis* Guenther, 1879 (Duke of York Island); and *dipsadides* Ogilby, 1891 (Fly River, New Guinea). Barbour described *clarki* in 1914 from the Murray Islands, and Stull described *kinghorni* in 1933 (*Occas. Papers Mus. Zoo., Univ. Mich.*, No. 267: 3) from Lake Barrine, Queensland. None of the names presently are considered valid, but if the species ever is split there certainly is no shortage of names.

The Scrub Python has at various times been placed in *Liasis* and *Morelia*, but McDowell considered it to be part of a transition series, *Python reticulatus>P. timoriensis>P. amethistinus*, on the basis of many skull and scalation characters. It also is closely related to *P. boeleni*, with which it agrees in many features of head scalation.

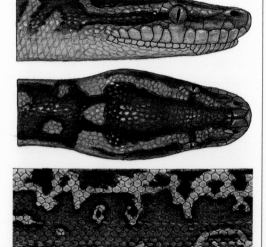

Head and midbody views of *P. anchietae.*

PYTHON ANCHIETAE
Angolan Python

The Angolan Python is the most uncommonly available African python and the most poorly known. Its restricted distribution in combination with political turmoil in half the range and highly restrictive export regulations in the other half has meant that it is almost unavailable to individual collectors. The species is easily told by the distinctive head pattern in combination with the irregular body pattern and the many small raised scales on top of the head.

Description

The Angolan Python is a cylindrical brownish snake with a rather flattened back and a small, flattened head. It seldom exceeds a meter in length and is not known to reach 2 meters. The snout is rounded. The tail is about 10% of the total length.

From above, the head is covered with small rounded scales that are raised and somewhat bead-like. The internasals and one pair of prefrontals are the only scales that are well-developed, and both are separated by two or three rows of small scales. From the side, the nostril is large and dorsally situated, there are many large and small scales (the loreals) between the eye and the nostril, and the eye is surrounded by a ring of small scales. There are about 14 supralabials, five of them with pits (three anterior

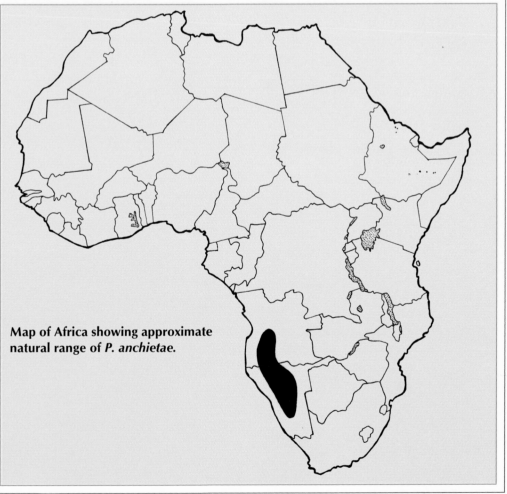

Map of Africa showing approximate natural range of *P. anchietae.*

Angolan Pythons make their homes in the rocky deserts of southwestern Africa, where the temperatures are incredibly variable. Photo by M. Burger.

ones very large).

The dorsal scales at midbody are in 57 to 61 rows. There are some 253 to 267 ventral scales and 46 or 47 pairs of subcaudals.

The hemipenis is about 30mm long and simple, with indistinct papillae (awns) at the ends of the poorly defined lobes. The sulcus is divided about 10mm from the base, and there are only a few poorly defined flounces. The hemipenes resemble those of *P. regius* but have a shorter base. Probes extend about 12 subcaudals in males.

Adults are reddish brown, rather faded and dull in appearance, with black-edged whitish bars and spots in an irregular pattern. The head is reddish brown with a distinctive black-edged white stripe running from the nostril back through the eye to above the corner of the mouth and then turning abruptly toward the nape. When the pattern is fully developed, the head appears brown above with a complete white triangle around the edges. More commonly the white stripe is broken or even absent across the back of the head. Often there is a single brown scale over the eye interrupting the white stripe, and there generally is a large but indistinct whitish spot (sometimes two or even three) at the center of the head behind the level of the eyes. The upper lip is whitish to the lower edge of the eye. The belly is yellowish white with a few brown blotches along the sides. Juveniles are bright chocolate brown with bright yellow markings.

Typical adults seem to be about 1.5 meters long, with a maximum recorded total length of 1.8 meters. Hatchlings are about 45 to 50 cm in length and weigh over 60 grams.

Natural Variation

There are no indications that there is significant variation in scale counts over the range of the species. The color pattern varies considerably from individual to

Above: Profile of *P. anchietae* showing the very broken and granular head scales. This feature is found in most of the African pythons. Photo by K. H. Switak. *Below: P. anchietae* must be considered a close relative of the Ball Python, *P. regius.* The snakes are similar in shape, occur fairly close to each other, and have similar behavior patterns. Photo by K. H. Switak.

individual, but the snake always remains brownish with a black-edged white pattern. The white bars tend to be very irregular across the back but often isolate large squarish to rectangular brown areas. The white bars may fuse together on the lower sides and produce a broken white stripe along the side. Typically there are some white spots irregularly scattered over the back and especially dense on the tail and posterior body.

desert.

Angolan Pythons are very gentle animals that are not prone to bite and often hide the head within coils of the body. They feed on birds and small mammals in nature and hide in burrows under rocks for cover. Little is known of the species in either nature or captivity, but natural egg-laying appears to occur during November, when females lay about five large (62 X 37mm) white rounded eggs. The female coils about the eggs and through shivering maintains a temperature about 5 degrees higher than the surrounding air. Incubation takes about 60 to 70 days.

Despite their stocky build, Angolan Pythons are powerful constrictors. They feed heavily on rodents and birds in nature. Photo by K. H. Switak.

This species seldom is exported and appears to be uncommon in nature. The area in which it occurs is sparsely settled, and Angola has been in a state of civil war for many years. Namibia currently prohibits the export of this species.

Natural History

This is a species of dry, rocky habitats at elevations between 750 and 1900 meters inland from the coast from central Angola to southern Namibia. This area is notorious for variable temperatures over the course of the year, from 55°C (123°F) during summer days to below freezing during the winter nights. There is little rainfall, and the area can be considered rocky

Husbandry

Only a few zoos and individuals have maintained Angolan Pythons over any period of time. They are relatively easy to keep and do well in small quarters. Most are ravenous feeders, and they may become overweight if fed as much

supraocular is much larger than the others. The scales at the back of the head are small and bumpy, and there may be a few larger oval scales scattered among them just behind the frontal. From the side, the nasal scale is large and protuberant. It is followed by a large number (20 or more) of small loreals and about three small preoculars. There are six or more small postoculars that are not distinct from the rest of the scales at the back of the head. The supralabials number 14 or 15, numbers seven and eight entering the eye and the first three with an oblique pit. There are about 16 or 17 infralabials, five to seven posterior labials shallowly pitted.

The body scales are in about 45 rows at midbody, with a formula of 41-45-30 in the holotype. All the scales above the first four or five rows are roughened with distinct keels that are strongest on the middorsal scales. In the holotype there are 298 ventrals and 83 subcaudals. The anal scale is entire, and most of the subcaudals are divided.

The body is pale yellowish tan marked with brown blotches and saddles. The head is brown, with a weakly defined yellowish stripe from the nostril through the eye to above the angle of the jaws in some specimens and indistinct yellowish blotches in others. There are many (to about 80) narrow brown bars, blotches, or saddles across the back, most with very irregular edges, alternating with equally irregular vertical bars and blotches on the

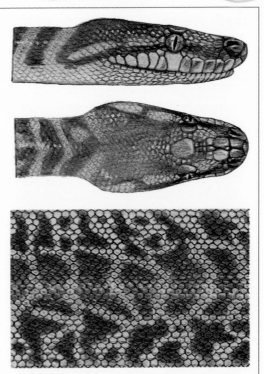

Head and midbody views of *P. carinatus*.

sides. The colors may be more contrasting posteriorly than anteriorly. There is no black in the pattern, even as scattered scales, in the specimens so far observed. The belly is creamy white with scattered brown smudges.

The known specimens include two adults about 2 meters long and one of about 1.4 meters. One subadult about 800mm has been observed.

Natural Variation

As usual with pythons with fragmented head scales, there seems to be quite a bit of individual variation in details of shield sizes and numbers. The color pattern is equally variable though always obviously similar to a carpet python.

Natural History

So far the species is known only from the lower parts of the Mitchell and Hunter Rivers in extreme northern Western Australia. They all are from patches of relict rain forest among vast expanses of sandstone plateaus. Limited observations indicate they are highly arboreal, and one specimen was seen hanging from a tree over a mammal trail, obviously waiting for prey. The front teeth are especially long, as in *P. viridis*, and may be an adaptation for quick strikes at moving mammal prey. The species has been observed active at night.

The rarity of the species may indicate that it is restricted to disappearing patches of rain forest. Certainly it is distinctive enough in many features of scalation to have been isolated for many years. Of course, few collectors venture into the area where it has been seen or collected, and it might prove to be a quite common nocturnal species in an area very difficult to access.

Husbandry

This species so far has not been kept in captivity, but it probably can be kept much like a carpet python.

Taxonomic History

Python carinatus was described by L. A. Smith in 1981 (*Rec. West. Aust. Mus.*, 9(2): 220-222) from a single specimen 1975mm long taken at Mitchell River Falls, Western Australia in 1973. Weigel and Russel (1993) recorded the third specimen, illustrated it in color, and detailed the collecting trip that led to its discovery near the mouth of the Hunter River. This paper makes for interesting reading not so much for details of the python (which are few) as for the discussion of the difficulties of collecting in this area, including lack of water, crocodiles, and being sure to be at the helicopter rendezvous by the proper day.

PYTHON CURTUS
Blood Python

Until recently, few Blood Pythons were available to hobbyists, but in the last few years specimens of all three described subspecies have entered the hobby. This species has a reputation for being vicious and striking at the least provocation, though some specimens appear to be more even-tempered. The species is readily recognized by the head with large shields above, a broad dark stripe behind the eye, a narrow whitish stripe angled back from the eye, and an exceptionally stout body with a small, slender tail.

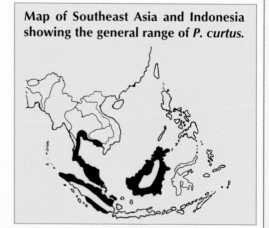

Map of Southeast Asia and Indonesia showing the general range of *P. curtus*.

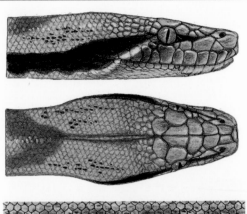

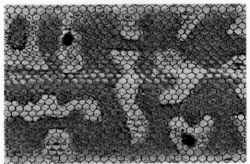

Head and midbody views of *P. curtus.*

Description

Blood Pythons are obese, flattened cylindrical snakes with small, very triangular heads and tiny tails that are 10% or less of the total length.

From above, the rostral scale is distinctly visible and followed by a pair of squarish internasals; there are two pairs of large prefrontals before the large frontal, which has a vertical seam down the center; and there are several pairs of parietal scales. The supraocular scale is large and may be divided into two smaller shields. From the side, there are several large scales near the nostril and many (nine or more) large and small loreal scales before the large preocular, which is largely dorsal in position and has several small scales (secondary preoculars) between it and the supralabials. There are one or two postoculars. The supralabials number 10 or 11, the first and second deeply pitted, and there are about 18 or 19 infralabials, about three pitted anteriorly and three to five shallowly pitted posteriorly. The eye may be separated from the supralabials by a row of small suboculars or two supralabials may enter the orbit.

The scales are in about 53 to 57 rows at midbody (typically with a formula of 51-55-33, 51 rows one

Many Blood Pythons are sharply marked animals. The colors vary greatly between individuals. Photo by W. P. Mara.

head length behind the head, 55 at midbody, and 33 one head length before the vent). The ventrals vary from about 158 to 175, and there are 28 to 32 pairs of subcaudals.

The hemipenes are broad distally with a pair of short and indistinct awns or tubercles; the sulcus bifurcates at about half the length of the organ, and there are a few flounces. The hemipenes bear a strong resemblance to those of *P. regius* and *P. anchietae.* Males probe to about nine subcaudals.

Color and pattern are quite variable, but generally the body is

The bottom animal is *P. curtus brongersmai*, and the one on top belongs to one of the other two subspecies, probably *P. c. breitensteini* judging by color. Photo by I. Francais.

the neck and a narrow whitish oblique stripe back from the eye.

Adults typically are about 1.2 to 1.5 meters long, with a few reaching 2 meters; there apparently is a record of a specimen 3 meters long.

reddish, blackish, or golden brown above and on the sides, with a series of rounded, elongated paler golden brown to yellowish spots down the center of the back, these often variably fused into a broken stripe. The sides bear alternating dark and pale (gray to golden) vertical bars, the pale bars often ending in a large dark spot; sometimes the sides are mostly dark or mostly pale with just irregularly placed ocellated dark spots. The top of the head is a clean pale brown, yellowish, red, or grayish black with a narrow dark line from the nape toward the snout; commonly the median line has a pair of short brown branches above the eye and a longer pair before the nape, as well as being wider near the nape and containing within it a pale area. The side of the head usually is darker than the top, but the area before the eye often appears unmarked. There is a narrowly pointed band running back from the eye to the side of

Natural Variation

Besides a great deal of individual variation in color and pattern, there also is significant variation in scalation. This variation has led to the description of three subspecies whose ranges and extent of variation are not perfectly known. They break into two groups.

In *P. c. brongersmai* from extreme southern Thailand (and possibly adjacent Laos and Cambodia but with just a few records that possibly are based on imported specimens), the Malayan Peninsula, and the northern coast of Sumatra and adjacent islands, there are two supraoculars on each side, generally more than 170 ventral scales, loreal scales of mixed sizes, and a distinctly dark reddish body coloration (the color of dried blood). In the two island subspecies (*P. c. curtus* from southern Sumatra and *P. c. breitensteini* from the island of Borneo) there is only one

Telling the subspecies of Blood Pythons apart relies mainly on head scalation. Top: *P. c. curtus.* It has one supraocular and a golden-brown base color. Photo by K. H. Switak. Center: *P. c. breitensteini.* This animal has one supraocular and a dark, purple-brown base color. Photo by W. P. Mara. Bottom: *P. c. brongersmai.* This snake has two supraoculars, and at least one labial scale entering the eye. Photo by R. D. Bartlett.

supraocular on each side, the ventrals tend to number about 160 to 170, the loreals usually include a strip of tiny scales running from the nostril to the lower preocular, and the body color varies from golden tan to grayish brown. Additionally, in *P. c. brongersmai* one or two supralabials usually enter the lower margin of the eye, while in the other subspecies there are small suboculars separating the eye from the supralabials. There is no evidence that *brongersmai* intergrades with *curtus* where the two might come into contact in eastern Sumatra, while *curtus* and

common name Blood Python; the other two subspecies perhaps are better known as Short-tailed Pythons. However, I've always thought the name Blood Python referred to the vicious tempers of wild-caught adults of all the forms and their tendency to draw blood whenever handled, so I'm retaining Blood Python for the entire species.

Natural History

The Blood Python is a sedentary species of swampy lowlands, especially marshes and river valleys. It tends to lie in the mud and dense vegetation, sometimes partially covered with mud, and waits for prey to walk by. It feeds mostly on small mammals and can easily take prey the size of a guinea pig. In its natural range from the Malayan Peninsula and adjacent Thailand over much of

Blood Pythons need very high humidity and a soft, loose substrate if they are to thrive in captivity. Photo by I. Francais.

breitensteini are very similar and differ mostly in color (*curtus* dark grayish, *breitensteini* golden brown). It might not be unreasonable to consider *brongersmai* a full species, but the species as a whole remains too poorly collected to be sure that isolation really exists.

Only *brongersmai* has a blood red color and truly deserves the

Sumatra and Borneo, the humidity is constantly high (well over 75%) and the temperature averages at least 27°C (81°F) throughout the year, with only small drops at night.

This species has a reputation as one of the most unpredictable and often vicious of the pythons. Its small head and very stout body make it hard to handle, and bites

Diamond Python, *P. s. spilotus*, is closest geographically to the east, but it is very different in color and pattern.

The presence of *imbricatus* so far from the nearest relatives is the result of simple isolation following the drying of the center of Australia. Though weakly differentiated in color, pattern, and scale counts from *P. spilotus*, the combination of obvious isolation and morphological distinctions (I am not aware of biochemical tests involving this species as yet) fulfills the requirements for a good evolutionary species.

PYTHON MOLURUS
Asian Rock Python

The most familiar python almost certainly is the gigantic Asian Rock Python, which appears to be about as common in the terrarium hobby as the Boa Constrictor. Also known as the Indian (Light Phase) Python and the Burmese (Dark Phase) Python, this is one of the few giant snakes that is tame enough to use in exhibitions such as snake charming and with the snake dancers of carnivals and arcades. Most adults are at least 3.6 meters long and weigh in excess of 30 kilograms, with truly monstrous examples of at least 9.2 meters (31 feet) being recorded.

Description

A very heavy-bodied snake in adults, more slender in juveniles, the head rather thick and moderately distinct from the

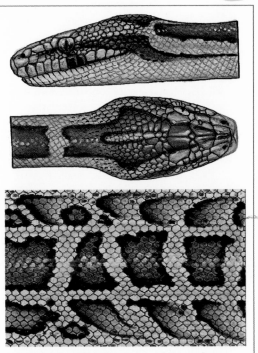

Head and midbody views of *P. molurus*.

neck. The tail is over 12% of the total length and strongly prehensile. The scales gleam with a strong iridescence, especially when the animal is freshly molted.

Seen from above, the nostrils are dorsally directed and each pierces a large nasal scale. The nasals are separated by a pair of small but distinct internasals that are followed by a pair of large, vaguely rectangular prefrontals. A second pair of prefrontals, much smaller and often broken into several smaller scales, lies between the anterior prefrontals and the paired frontals that are very similar to the anterior prefrontals in size and shape. There is a single large supraocular over each eye. The rostral scale, like that of most other pythons, has two deep pits.

From the side, the nasal scale is followed by several loreal scales of varying sizes and shapes; there usually are two preoculars and three or four postoculars, but they may be irregular. The first and second supralabials are deeply pitted; there are 11 to 13 supralabials and 16 to 18 infralabials. Several anterior and posterior infralabials are shallowly and indistinctly pitted.

The dorsal scales are in 61 to 75 rows at midbody. The ventral scales vary from 245 to 270, and there are 58 to 73 pairs of subcaudals.

The hemipenes are shallowly but obviously bilobed and have long, distinct awns at the tips of the lobes. There usually is a single flounce on the stem, and the sulcus bifurcates at about half the length of the organ. A male will probe 10 to 16 subcaudals. There are 36 diploid chromosomes (2N=36), with 16 macrochromosomes and 20 microchromosomes.

Asian Rock Pythons are pale tan to yellowish cream in color, occasionally darker, with about 30 to 40 large squarish dark brown saddles over the back. The saddles are outlined with black and may vary greatly in shape, sometimes being reduced to narrow rectangles or triangles or even split into irregular pairs. On each side is a series of smaller brown, usually elongated spots that alternate with the saddles. There is much variation in details of shape, number, and color of the dorsal pattern. The side of the head has a dark brown, usually pointed bar extending from the front of the eye and a broader, black-edged band extending from the back of the eye to beyond the angle of the jaws; a brown wedge is under the eye and helps outline a broad whitish spot that runs from under the eye to the jaws.

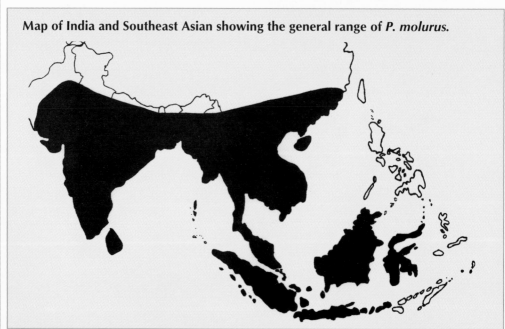

Map of India and Southeast Asian showing the general range of *P. molurus*.

Asian Rock Pythons are at the top of the food chain in their natural range. Their wild prey includes wild pigs, goats, and deer, but they usually take smaller fare. Photo by M. Burger.

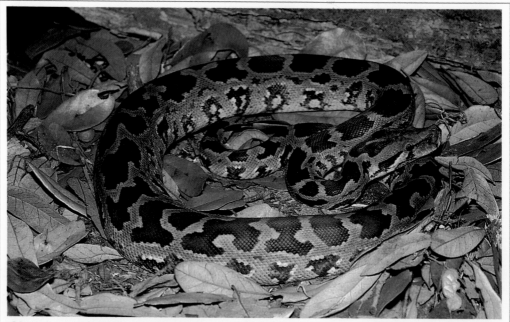

This Asian Rock Python originated in Sri Lanka. The irregular saddles are typical of the specimens from that island. Hobbyists often designate these animals as *P. m. "pimbura."* Photo by R. D. Bartlett.

On top of the head is a large brown arrowhead, hollow in the center, that begins on the nape and extends to at least the area of the eyes and sometimes to the snout. The belly is yellowish white with scattered dark spots and blotches that are heaviest under the tail.

Adult females are about 3.6 to 6 meters long, with males maturing at about 2.4 to 2.7 meters in length. A heavy female about 3.6 meters long may weigh over 25 kilograms, while a wild-caught specimen 4.5 meters long weighed 52 kilos. The maximum length long has been stated to be almost 9.2 meters (30 to 31 feet), but like other large snake records this is hard to confirm. Probably few specimens today exceed 7 to 7.5 meters (23 to 24.6 feet) in total length.

Natural Variation

Like some of the other snakes that long have been known to western naturalists, the Asian Rock Python has been described many times under many scientific names. Currently only two names are considered to represent valid subspecies, with some workers believing a third subspecies is valid. The two valid subspecies are the western, light, or Indian form, *P. m. molurus*, which is best recognized by the combination of supralabials six or seven entering the lower edge of the eye and the brown arrow on top of the head indistinct anterior to the eyes. This subspecies ranges from Pakistan over India and Sri Lanka northeastward to Bengal and Assam. To the east, in Burma and Thailand, southward through the Malayan Peninsula to Java,

Borneo, and the Celebes (Sulawesi), occurs the Burmese or dark form, *P. m. bivittatus*, which has the brown arrowhead on top of the head complete or nearly so and extending to the snout plus has a row of small suborbitals separating the eye from the supralabials. Additionally, as a general rule the brown saddles of the Indian subspecies are paler than those of the Burmese subspecies. The Asian Rock Pythons in Sri Lanka have been described as a distinct subspecies (*pimbura*) that is not recognized by most workers; it is supposed to be darker than most Indian pythons and its brown body blotches are very irregular in shape and seldom form uniform saddles, tending more toward triangles and odd forms. The Sri Lankan form is supposed to have fewer brown saddles than Indian pythons, but this has not been confirmed by later workers. Additionally, it may have the arrowhead even more erased than in Indian specimens, giving the appearance of just a shallow fork on the nape. This form is said to be especially hard to tame and strikes with little provocation.

Natural History

Asian Rock Pythons range from Pakistan over all of India from Bengal and Assam to Sri Lanka, eastward through Burma and Thailand over the Malayan Peninsula. It also has been recorded from Sumatra, Java, Borneo, and the Celebes, as well

The Burmese Python has been bred frequently in captivity, and various color and pattern mutations have been selected for. This is an amelanistic (albino) variety. Photo by M. Burger.

as rarely in southern China, Hainan, and most of the rest of Southeast Asia. However, this animal long has featured in native cultures of the region and it is suspected that it has been moved around by man. Its rarity in Southeast Asia east of the Burma-Thailand-Malayan Peninsula area may be due to erratic human introductions and its failure to compete with the Reticulated Python. The same also may be true of its spotty distribution in the Indonesian area.

Like many other large pythons, the Asian Rock is a species most at home in warm, very humid areas near lakes, rivers, canals, and other large bodies of water. It is a better swimmer than a mover on land, and it can stay submerged for about half an hour. Often it has been seen relaxing (or waiting for prey) in shallow water with just the nostrils projecting above the surface of the water. It moves slowly on land and is considered to be relatively innocuous, attempting to hide when discovered and not biting unless greatly stressed. Some specimens, however, seem to always be vicious, though most are relatively tame. The large size of this snake makes it possible for it to take prey of all types, including not only mammals and birds but also monitor lizards. It repeatedly has been incriminated in cases of human deaths in its native range, usually being said to take babies and small children left unattended near water. Some of these stories certainly are true, and the species has under unusual circumstances occasionally injured and even killed adult hobbyists and other handlers. Big snakes, no matter how tame

New patterns occasionally crop up unexpectedly. This uniquely garbed Burmese Python was captured on the Malay Peninsula. Photo by M. Bacon.

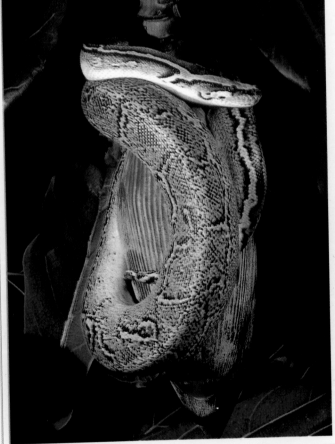

they may seem, must be considered potentially dangerous.

In Pakistan and probably much of northern India these pythons hibernate from October through February, when mating is thought to occur. The eggs are laid two months later and hatch in another two or three months. The young have been found in August and are about 50 to 60 cm in length. As usual, the female coils around her eggs to protect them and also shivers to increase the temperature within her coils. It is likely that pythons from Burma and Thailand and points south, areas with more constant temperatures and no real winter, do not hibernate.

The large size and rather complacent personality of the Asian Rock Python have led to it being a favorite prey of skin

The top of the snout is pale in Indian Pythons, while the Burmese have a well-formed arrowhead marking. Photo by I. Francais.

hunters in southern Asia and India. Additionally, it is considered to be quite good to eat, and its internal organs are supposed to have medicinal value. Frankly, it is hard to understand how this python has survived until today, and in some areas (such as Sri Lanka) it may be in danger of immediate extirpation.

Burmese Pythons are one of the most popular of all pythons in the hobby, despite the gigantic proportions they can reach. Photo by A. Both.

The western (Indian, light) subspecies, *P. m. molurus*, is considered an endangered, species and possessing or trading in this form requires permits and a lot of work going through red tape. It has almost disappeared from the American and European markets except for a few specimens in zoo collections that rarely make it to the hobby.

Husbandry

Python molurus bivittatus, the common Burmese Python, has been bred in large numbers for at least two decades and today is an affordable and easily obtainable species. Unfortunately, many hobbyists purchase a specimen when it is only 60 to 120 cm long and fail to consider that it will grow to many meters in just a few years. Large snakes are difficult to house, expensive to feed, and probably are in violation of local laws if you live in dozens of cities in the United States and Europe. Though beautiful snakes and often gentle, you must consider all the negatives before making a purchase.

Maintenance of this species is simple, as it requires only a large terrarium heated to about 30°C (86°F) or so, a high humidity brought about by regular misting and a large water bath in the cage, and a regular menu of mammals of suitable size. Most are not especially aggressive, though they may form a hierarchy with a dominant male controlling other specimens in the colony. Of course, only a zoo or commercial breeder is likely to have the space

A very rare variety of the Burmese Python is the calico. This 14 foot-long female is one of only four such animals known to exist. Photo by M. Walls. Courtesy of Keith McPeek.

to establish a colony of these large snakes.

Breeding has become relatively simple, though again the large size of the adults (about 2.7 meters and up in males, 3.6 meters and up in females) makes it difficult for a hobbyist to maintain a pair or trio. These pythons breed without a winter cooling, though a short cool period is not harmful. Clutches of the female. Generally hobbyists remove the eggs from the female after a day or two, taking care not to separate eggs that have stuck together, and incubate them at 100% humidity and about 32°C (90°F) for about 60 days. The young may stay in the egg shell for several hours or a few days and generally take their first meal after their first shed, perhaps a week or so after hatching. They

This uncommon variety with the pattern reduced to spots is know as a leopard Burmese. It apparently is the result of breeding normal individuals with patternless ones. Photo by D. Dube.

8 to 30 eggs (occasionally more, with communal nests of over 100 eggs being recorded) are laid between March and May following mating between November and February. The eggs are very large (125 X 65 mm), creamy white to pale tan, and look a lot like ostrich eggs in form. They may be adhesive or non-adhesive but usually are laid in a deep bed of damp peat and then brooded by feed readily on mice and rats and later on larger prey.

Maturity is reached by an age of three. Captive-bred specimens commonly live 10 to 15 years, and there are records of more than 20 years in captivity.

With so many specimens of *Python molurus bivittatus* having been bred over the last two decades, it was only a matter of time until varieties appeared.

The labyrinth Burmese is a striking animal in which the normal saddles tend to be reduced into partial stripes. Photo by A. Both.

Today albinos are relatively common and inexpensive snakes, so much so that some hobbyists fear that continued breeding of this variety will lead to depression of the python market. Another common variety is the green or patternless Burmese, in which the snake has the pattern reduced to rounded pale brown lozenges (and sometimes a middorsal stripe) on a creamy tan background with a distinct moss green tinge; large adults become quite dull tan with an indistinct pattern and little greenish tinge. Greens have been crossed with albinos. The labyrinth or jungle morph is a striking but very variable form that is produced at least in part by crossing an albino with a green. The jungle tends to be bright brown above, very pale on the sides, with long dark brown elongated ovals on the back and irregular vertical dark brown bars on the side; this may be the most stunning color variety in any cultivated snake. A new variant, dubbed "granite," is covered with small, very irregular brown spots and reticulations; it is being commercially produced. Additionally, leucistic (alabaster white) and axanthic (lacking all yellow) mutations are known, along with various distorted patterns. There is a record of a Burmese Python being hybridized with a Reticulated Python and producing 25 living young. The offspring looked like neither parent though more similar to a jungle Burmese in the greatly reduced appearance of the pattern; the head pattern was distinctly reduced compared to the *molurus* parent. Doubtless more mutations (and hybrids) await breeders of these pythons.

Taxonomic History

Python molurus was described by Linnaeus in 1758 in the 10th edition of his *Systema Naturae*, but the snake was well-known for centuries before this. It rapidly acquired a multitude of synonyms based largely on details of color pattern variations, all of which today are carefully ignored. Schneider in 1801 (*Hist. Amph.*, 2) described the Indian *ordinata*, *cinerea*, *castanea*, *albicans*, and *orbiculata*, while the names *boaeformis*, *bora*, *tigris*, *trivittatus*, *intermedia*, and *ocellatus* were added by various authors over the next hundred years, with Deraniyagala in 1945 (*Spolia Zeylan.*, 24: 105) adding *pimbura* to the long list of probable synonyms. Kuhl in 1820 first described the Burmese Python as a full species, *Python bivittatus*, in *Beitr. Zool. vergl. Anat.*, 1: 94, the type locality later being restricted to Java (where the species may be introduced and not native); *sondaica* Werner, 1899, was described from Sumatra and appears to be a synonym of *bivittatus*.

Curiously, no one ever seems to have tried to study variation of this species over the entire range (it is notoriously difficult to study many specimens of very large snakes), but today so many snakes may have been moved about by man that it might be impossible to accurately determine the relationships of the forms. The subspecies *molurus* and *bivittatus* may intergrade in northern Burma, but even this is uncertain. Political problems throughout the region may today make adequate collections impossible. The close similarity of the two subspecies in structure and color pattern, and the seeming lack of a gap in their distribution, are fair indications of subspecies relationships rather than full species.

Hobbyists should be aware that specimens sold as *bivittatus*, the

The Indian subspecies of the Asian Rock Python is protected by international law. When offered for sale, documentation of their origin and legality should be obtained. Photo by A. Norman.

common form in the hobby, probably represent a mixed gene pool of ancestors that may have been pure *bivittatus* plus typical *molurus*, and possibly the Sri Lankan form (the doubtful *pimbura*) as well. There are few "pure" *Python molurus bivittatus* in the hobby today, and it is no use deceiving yourself as to the scientific usefulness of specimens in the herpetocultural hobby.

PYTHON NATALENSIS
Lesser Rock Python

The Lesser Rock Python generally is treated as a subspecies of the African Rock Python, *Python sebae*, but the ranges of the two barely overlap, there is some evidence that they occur together at a few spots without signs of obvious hybridization, and there are

---

Head and midbody views of *P. natalensis.*

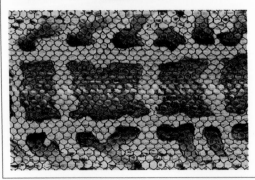

significant differences in color patterns and head scalation between the forms. It should be noted that subspecies are not recognized in any other African pythons.

Description

A large, cylindrical python with a broad head distinct from the neck. It is generally similar to *Python sebae* in appearance, differing in many details of scalation and color pattern. The snout is rather narrowly rounded, the eye small and with a vertically elliptical pupil.

The nostrils are dorsolateral in position but visible from above. The rostral shield is narrowly triangular from above. The large pair of internasals is followed by two pairs of prefrontals. The rest of the top of the head is covered with irregular scales; there is no distinct frontal visible even as a fragmented shield (as is the case in *P. sebae*) and the supraoculars are fragmented. From the side, there are many small loreals (fewer and larger in *P. sebae*) and a ring of about 8 to 13 scales around the orbit, which is separated from the supralabials. There are 10 to 16 supralabials (two of them pitted) and 17 to 24 infralabials (two distinctly pitted anteriorly and three or four shallowly pitted posteriorly).

The midbody scales are in 78 to 99 rows. There are 260 to 291 ventrals and 63 to 84 pairs of subcaudals. The hemipenis is over 50mm long and shallowly forked, the forks ending in small awns (tubercles). The sulcus bifurcates at about 60% of the length of the organ. There are three chevron-like flounces on the back of the hemipenis.

The body is tan to olive or grayish in general color with a series of large, irregular dark brown blotches and saddles outlined in black. The saddles are variously fused and tend to be more distinct anteriorly than posteriorly. The smaller blotches on the sides may fuse with the saddles or with each other to form a very broken line. The top of the tail usually is blotched. The top of the head is covered with a dark brown triangle that covers most of the head and is rather weakly contrasted with the whitish stripe that runs from the nostril through the top of the eye onto the side of the neck. From the side there is a narrow dark streak in front of the eye and a broader (about equal to diameter of eye) dark streak behind the eye that stops at the angle of the jaws. The upper lip is weakly marked with just a few dark spots. (In *P. sebae* the pattern on top of the head is strongly contrasted and the side of the snout is mostly dark with large dark areas on the supralabials.) The belly is whitish with scattered dark specks and

Map of Africa showing the general natural range of *P. natalensis*.

blotches that may fuse into a dark line under the tail.

This is a distinctly smaller form than *P. sebae*, most specimens being about 3 to 5 meters long (females larger), with a maximum length of about 5.6 meters, certainly no more than 6 meters at the outside. (*P. sebae* reaches over 9 meters in length.)

Natural Variation

The differences between *P. natalensis* and *P. sebae* in head scalation and color pattern are consistent with species level in this genus and certainly are more than the equivalent of species in the Australian pythons. The two species appear to be sympatric near Mwingi and Nairobi, Kenya, and only a few intermediate specimens have been reported from Tanzania. Since the ability to interbreed is a primitive character that probably is meaningless in interpreting speciation when it occurs over a very narrow front, it seems logical to give *natalensis* full specific rank.

Natural History

The Lesser Rock Python is found in savannas, usually near large bodies of permanent water, throughout southern Africa from southern Angola to southern Tanzania and Kenya south through eastern South Africa (now locally extinct in many areas); it is absent from the southwestern part of South Africa and most of Namibia.

Like other large pythons, the Lesser Rock feeds on small to relatively large mammals and birds and the occasional reptile. It is considered to be one of the more vicious pythons, striking rapidly and repeatedly, and is capable of severe bites.

One way to tell the two African rock pythons apart is to look at the labial scales. *P. natalensis* has pale labials when compared to *P. sebae* and lacks the white triangles below the eyes. Photo by K. H. Switak.

Females tend to be larger than males and mature in about five years. They lay large batches of 30 to 100 eggs about the size of an orange in clutches protected in disused mammal burrows, caves, and other protected areas. Though the female coils around the eggs during the 65- to 80-day incubation period, they are reported not to shiver to raise the temperature of the eggs above air temperature. The young are about 600mm long at hatching and are more brightly and distinctly patterned than the adults, as is common in most pythons.

Though now protected in South Africa and Namibia, this large python still is harvested for skins in the rest of its range and tends to disappear from near densely inhabited areas. Possession of this species (and *P. sebae*, with which it is mixed in the legal literature) in South Africa requires a special permit and attention to detailed housing requirements. Once more widely distributed over southern Africa, it now is gone from most of the Cape even where suitable habitat exists, and its future is not certain.

Although found in semi-arid areas, *P. natalensis* frequents standing bodies of water and soaks for long periods of time. Photo by M. Burger.

Husbandry

This species seems to be generally unavailable in the terrarium hobby, and when it is imported it has a bad reputation. It can be kept like any other large python, and definitely needs careful handling.

Limited reproduction has been attained in this species. When it has been bred, it has been over-wintered at slightly lower than normal temperatures and mating has occurred in February, with eggs being laid about two months later. The eggs laid in captivity have been 80 to 100mm long and have numbered about 20 in a clutch. Incubation at 32°C (90°F) seems adequate.

Taxonomic History

Python natalensis was described by A. Smith in 1840 in his *Illustr. Zool. S. Africa*: pl. 9, giving the type locality as Port Natal (South Africa). Since the late 1800's the name has been treated

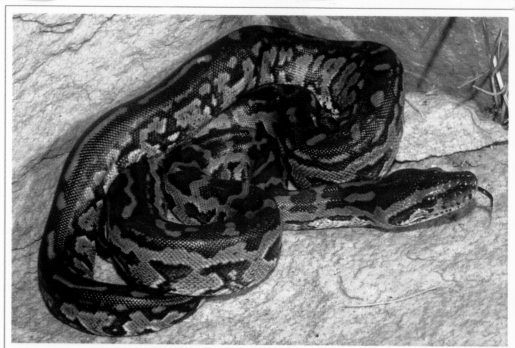

While it is a hardy snake, the Lesser Rock Python can not be considered a beginner's snake, due to its great size and bad disposition. Photo by M. Burger.

as a synonym or subspecies of *P. sebae* without any actually stated reason or comparison. Broadley (1984) seems to have been the first to actually compare the two forms in detail, although he tentatively considered *natalensis* to be a subspecies of *sebae*. The level of morphological distinction between the two forms plus the nearly allopatric ranges with good evidence of limited sympatry plus limited hybridization are forceful arguments for full species rank.

The doubtful *Python saxuloides* Miller & H. M. Smith (1979, *Bull. Maryland Herp. Soc.*, 15: 70-84) seems to be based on specimens of *natalensis* from Kenya, though there are small differences noted by Broadley. However, large pythons are notoriously variable in details of coloration and scalation, and it seems likely that

saxuloides is indeed a synonym of *natalensis*, perhaps from a population that has slightly differentiated.

PYTHON OENPELLIENSIS
Oenpelli Python

One of the "surprise" discoveries in Australian herpetology of the last few decades was the Oenpelli Python, a form somewhat similar to the Scrub Python in color and scalation but with many unique characters of the head and body scalation.

Description

The Oenpelli Python is a large, very slender, graceful python with a long tail (about 15% of total length), protruding eyes, and a narrow head distinct from the very slender neck. The head scales are somewhat distinct, and there are many small loreals. The eyes are silvery.

From above the snout is rather elongated and rounded, the deeply pitted rostral scale and nostrils barely visible. The internasals are small and squarish but distinct, and they are followed by a pair of much larger, distinct, squarish anterior prefrontals. The posterior prefrontals are represented by many large and small scales, typically over 20 in total, and the frontal is broken into about three fragments of nearly equal size. The supraoculars are large and generally split wholly or partially into two or three smaller scales. The parietals are greatly fragmented. From the side, the large nasal scale is followed by about 25 to 45 loreal scales of mixed sizes from rather large to tiny granules. There are three or four preoculars and five to seven postoculars. There are 15 to 17 supralabials, two or three entering the edge of the orbit. The first three supralabials have oblique pits. Of the 22 to 24 infralabials, the anterior ones are narrow and strap-like, the squarer posterior ones bearing pits on about six scales in a groove.

The middorsal scales are in 70 rows; there are about 53 rows one head length behind the head and 35 rows one head length before the vent. About half the dorsal scales are doubled, there being two scales in relation to each ventral. The ventral count is phenomenally high, 429 to 445,

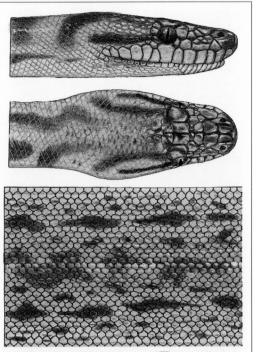

Head and midbody views of *P. oenpelliensis.*

as is the subcaudal count of 155 to 163 pairs.

The hemipenes are forked, there are seven flounces on each organ, and the sulcus is bifurcate. Males probe to about 15 subcaudals, but females are said to probe as much as ten subcaudals.

Map of Australia showing the general natural range of *P. oenpelliensis.*

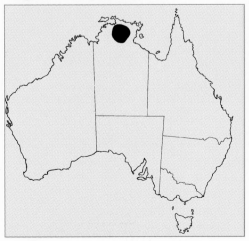

Because it was only recently discovered, little is known about the habits of *P. oenpelliensis*. However, it does appear to be common within its range. Photo by R. Hoser.

The coloration of adults is fairly variable, but it usually consists of a grayish to pale reddish tan background (intensity changeable with mood) and a whitish to pale yellow belly. There are four to six rows of irregular darker reddish brown blotches over the back, the largest blotch near the center of the back, the smallest above the ventrals. The tail may appear reticulated with brown. The head is pale brown, usually with some darker smudges and a narrow dark brown stripe back from the eye; another brown stripe may extend from above the eye to the back of the head on each side.

Hatchlings are reddish brown without an obvious pattern.

Typical adults are from 3 to 4 meters long, with a definite record of over 4.5 meters. There are repeated unconfirmed reports of specimens over 6 meters in length.

Natural Variation

As you might expect, the details of scale counts on the head vary considerably, but the large anterior prefrontals followed by a group of many smaller scales is constant. Some specimens appear to have the pits in the supralabials and rostral scale more shallow than others. Night coloration tends to be much paler than day coloration, with the blotches more contrasting. This appears to be one of the few species where hatchlings lack a distinct pattern and gain the adult pattern only with growth (as in *P. boeleni* and *P. amethistinus*).

Natural History

Though only described two decades ago, the Oenpelli Python appears to be a common and often noted python in its restricted range in Arnhem Land, the northern part of Australia's Northern Territory. The species apparently long has been known to the natives but simply escaped the observation of Europeans until recently. Much of its range is inside Kakadu National Park.

This large snake is associated with sandstone outcrops and open savanna forests. It has been seen feeding on pigeons in trees and has been wedged out of sandstone crevices. Specimens sometimes are taken crossing the

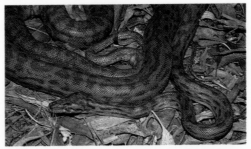

The protuberant eyes of *P. oenpelliensis* may allow some limited binocular vision. Photo by K. H. Switak.

highways. It appears to be a bird specialist, taking mostly birds in nature and often refusing mammals in captivity.

Females seem to lay clutches of six to ten large (120 X 50mm) white eggs between September and November. Hatchlings are about 800 to 900mm long and uniformly reddish brown without an obvious pattern. The pattern begins to appear with the first

Adult Oenpelli Pythons are very slender pythons, as would befit their semi-arboreal lifestyle. Photo by K. H. Switak.

shed two to three month after hatching (an exceptionally long interval between hatching and shedding).

Husbandry

Because this species is completely protected in Australia, very little is known about its keeping. A few specimens have been bred in captivity in the past in Australia and there may currently be a concerted effort to establish a breeding program there. The range of the species is largely in parks and aboriginal reserves, so no matter how common the species may be it cannot be collected.

If kept much like a Scrub Python the species should do fine in captivity, but it would seem that the species may like less humid conditions. Specimens at least eight to ten years old have bred in captivity, producing eggs that hatched in about 100 days. There has been a high rate of hatching failure and deformed young in the few breeding attempts.

Taxonomic History

Python oenpelliensis was first described by Gow in 1977 (*Aust. Zool.*, 19(2): 133-139) on the basis of two males, the holotype from 6.5 kilometers southwest of Oenpelli and the paratype from Little Nourlangie Rock, both in Arnhem Land. Both specimens were over 3.5 meters in length.

This species is exceptionally slender for a python, a fact reflected in the gigantic number of ventrals and subcaudals. Counts of 429 and 445 ventrals are recorded in *P. oenpelliensis*, while the next closest count is 346 in the related *P. amethistinus*. The eyes seem protuberant, and the loreal area is slightly concave, perhaps to allow forward vision.

PYTHON REGIUS
Ball Python

The most common python in the terrarium hobby certainly is the Ball Python, a species that not only is bred in some numbers in captivity but still is imported as cheap, stressed wild-caught animals. Commonly known as the Royal or Regal Python in the older hobby literature, it can be instantly recognized by the distinctive and almost invariable head pattern: solid brown above with sharply defined yellowish brown stripes on the side of the face. One of the smallest true

Head and midbody views of *P. regius*.

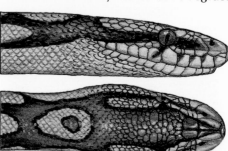
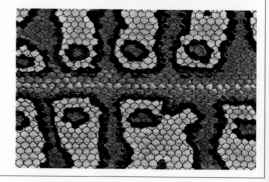

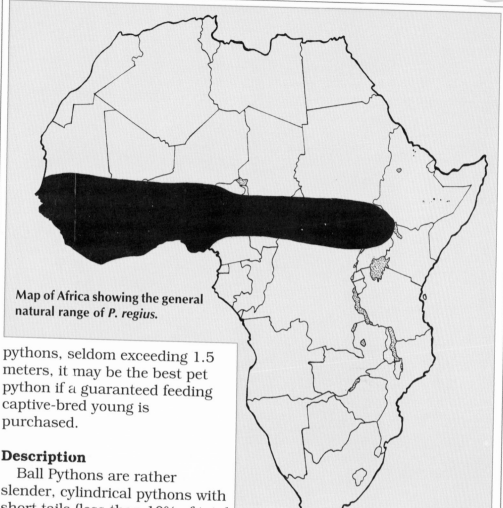

Map of Africa showing the general natural range of *P. regius*.

pythons, seldom exceeding 1.5 meters, it may be the best pet python if a guaranteed feeding captive-bred young is purchased.

Description

Ball Pythons are rather slender, cylindrical pythons with short tails (less than 10% of total length). The head is broad and quite distinct from the neck, while the snout appears broadly rounded. The eye is dark and of moderate size.

The nostrils are large and visible from above, the rostral scale is large and distinct, and a pair of strap-like internasals separates the nasal scales. The anterior prefrontals typically are large and distinct, and there may be a broken second pair behind them indicated by a row of irregularly broken scales. The frontal scale may be visible as usually two irregular large scales, or there may be a group of irregular scales of various sizes and shapes in its position. There may be a large and distinct supraocular or several broken scales over the eye. From the side, the large nasal scale is followed by a variable number of loreal scales of mixed sizes. There are two to four preoculars and three or four postoculars of varied sizes. The first four supralabials are deeply pitted and distorted, and there may be smaller pits in the next two as well. There are some 10 or 11 supralabials, the fifth or sixth either entering the eye or separated from it by a row of suboculars. The infralabials are smooth except for traces of pits in two or three posterior scales.

The dorsal scales are in 53 to 63 rows at midbody. There are 191 to 207 ventrals and 28 to 37 pairs of subcaudals. Interestingly, the anal plate may be entire (as normal for the genus) or divided.

The hemipenes are rather slender and not distinctly forked, each weak lobe ending in a small awn. The sulcus bifurcates above the middle of the organ. There is a strong flounce separating the base of the hemipenis from the distal portion, the flounce often forming a large papilla on the back surface. Males probe about ten subcaudals.

Though variable in details, the color pattern of *Python regius* is quite distinctive. The top of the head is dark brown, occasionally with a paler central area, and is defined to the side by a broad pale stripe that runs from above the nostril through the eye to the back of the head. The brown from the top of the head continues back along the sides of the neck and also puts out a rather broad band that continues forward above the supralabials into the lower edge of the eye; the face anterior to the eye typically has a broad, rather smudgy brown band over it. The posterior supralabials

Ball Pythons are one of the most heliophilic of the pythons, basking in direct sunlight for long periods of time. Photo by V. Jirousek.

This Ball Python is exhibiting the defensive posture typical for the species: rolling into a ball with its head in the middle. Photo by K. H. Switak.

This "reverse striped" phase is created by the golden-brown color from the sides extensively invading the black mid-dorsal stripe. Photo by D. Dube.

sides extending nearly to the center of the back. The nape and the top of the tail typically are pale. The belly is whitish to yellowish with a few scattered dark spots.

Most adult Ball Pythons are 0.9 to 1.4 meters long, with exceptional individuals slightly exceeding 2 meters.

Natural Variation

No subspecies are recognized in the Ball Python, though I am not aware of any detailed study of its variation. The major natural variation is in coloration, varying from nearly black to golden tan on a dull grayish to bright yellowish brown, and pattern, from a nearly unbroken dark middorsal stripe with regular narrow bands on the sides to a very broken pattern in which the middorsal stripe almost disappears and the pale color of the sides extends nearly to the middle of the back. The dark spots in the pale side areas may be paired, rounded, and not ocellated, or single, fused into a short band, and ocellated with distinct pale tan. The head pattern is quite constant, though the area in front of the eye may

are pale. The typical body pattern consists of a broad dark brown band down the middle of the body, this band sending out narrow vertical extensions over the sides. Often there is a pair of small dark spots enclosed between each pair of extensions. The background color varies from grayish to bright golden tan, and the dark middorsal stripe may be partially broken or irregularly indented by the pale color of the have a distinct dark band extending to the nostril, a broad brownish rectangle with irregular ventral edge, or be almost unmarked. The pale (usually yellowish) stripe from above the nostril through the eye appears not to vary.

Natural History

The Ball Python is a species of western Africa, extending from Senegal and the Gambia southward to Ghana and the Nigeria area and then eastward in a narrow band over the savannas to the Sudan and northern Uganda. It typically is a species of savanna edges, occupying rodent burrows during the day and hunting for gerbils and jerboas at night. Though it is most common in grassy areas near the edges of fields (where there are many rodents), it climbs well in shrubby terrain. Daytime temperatures often exceed 38°C (100°F) during the day with high humidities. The burrows are not much cooler than the surface temperature and may be more humid. Docile snakes that seldom bite, cornered Ball Pythons often form a tight round ball of coils with the head buried deep in the center of the ball. It has been stated that the ball is sometimes so regular that you can actually roll it down a plank, but more typically it is less regular. Many small pythons and boas produce a regular ball when disturbed, but *P. regius* is perhaps the most famous, and justly so.

Several pythons may occupy one burrow, though typically only one is found. Mating occurs during the dry season or winter (November to January), with egg-laying taking place a month or so later. By February the females are in their burrows (usually only one

Ball Pythons are dwellers of the African savannas, and, as such, they need warm keeping conditions with moderate humidity. They are very long-lived snakes. Photo by A. Both.

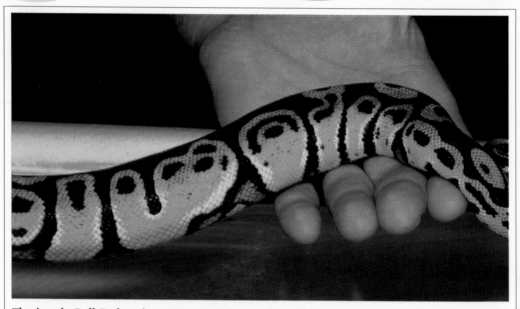

The jungle Ball Python is a very attractive snake with a strongly contrasting pattern. The normally brownish sides have brightened to an amber yellow. Photo by Photo by M. Walls.

female per burrow) with a clutch of about five large, very adhesive eggs. These take some two months to hatch, young appearing in late April. The incubation burrow, which assumedly is the same burrow occupied by the snake the rest of the year, may have a humidity of 86%, higher than that above ground, and a daytime temperature near 33 to 34°C (92 to 94°F), just 10 to 15 degrees cooler than the surface temperature. The burrows have small openings and may be only a few centimeters to over a meter deep.

Because of restrictions on importation of Boa Constrictors from tropical America, a few years ago the terrarium industry turned to the Ball Python as a source of small, cheap "giant snakes." The Ball Python is still the most inexpensive booid to purchase as an imported specimen, and it is imported by the tens of thousands. Many of these imports are captive-hatched from egg clutches taken from incubating females that are dug from their burrows and then released. The eggs are hatched in a sawdust pit under natural temperature and humidity, and the young are exported. Unfortunately, many imported Ball Pythons, both wild-caught adults and captive-hatched young, do not feed well and do not survive. In some areas of western Africa it is likely (though there are no real numbers to back up the contention) that repeated loss of most of the clutches each year may be leading to local extirpation of the Ball Python.

In nature many Ball Pythons probably live for over 10 years, and in captivity records of established specimens approaching 20 years are not uncommon. The record for the species, and perhaps for any snake, is a specimen kept in captivity for over 47 years.

Husbandry

If you get a captive-bred specimen that is eating mice, gerbils, or small rats, this is an easy species. An adult or two can be kept in a terrarium less than a meter long with a substrate of carpet. Some keepers prefer to avoid sand and other fine substrate materials because these may clog the pits in the upper labials and cause an infection. Keep the terrarium warm, over 28°C (82°C), humid, and provide a large water bowl. Mist the terrarium daily. The lid must, of course, be kept tightly latched. Ball Pythons spend most of their time resting in the security of a hide box, at least one of which always must be present in the terrarium. There should be a warmer basking area available.

Captive-breds typically feed readily on frozen and thawed mice and rat pups, though some individuals may insist on living prey. If you feed living rodents, remember that an unattended prey animal can inflict severe damage on a python in a confined space. It might be wise to provide, in addition to a dark, tight hide box, a raised climbing surface for your Ball Python. Feeding is preferentially at night, but captives often get used to taking food during the day as well.

Imports may not feed at all or may have to be force-fed. Some will take only gerbils, while others may prefer a specific color (sometimes white) of mouse. Imports often are heavily parasitized and in poor condition. Be wise, buy domestically produced captive-breds.

Captive reproduction is common in this species, but the small clutch size (almost always under ten eggs) prevents captive-breds from becoming more abundant in the market. The snakes, males determined by the larger spurs or by probing, are over-wintered at about 21 to 27°C (70 to 81°F), the coolest temperatures at night, for one to two months and then put together for mating. The eggs are laid about a month after mating,

Part of the attraction of Ball Pythons is that they are normally docile and easy to handle. Photo by A. Norman.

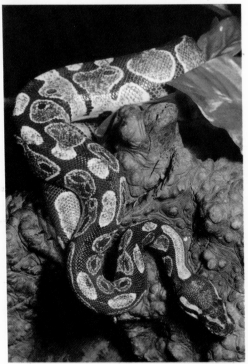

This is probably an axanthic Ball Python. Axanthism is a mutation causing the absence of yellow pigments. Photo by D. Dube.

average three to six per clutch, and are round, whitish, and about 50mm in diameter. The eggs stick together and are easily damaged if you try to pry them apart. They also become covered with the peat moss in which the female lays. Female Ball Pythons do not normally coil about their eggs and do not shiver to raise the temperature. Eggs incubated at about 32°C (90°F) hatch in approximately 60 days. They can be incubated at a relatively low humidity (65 to 75%) if the humidity is increased to almost 100% just before hatching. Hatchlings are about 350mm long and may not feed for over a week. If they do not feed at the end of their first month, force-feeding

may be necessary to get them started. They must be kept humid by frequent misting. Maturity is reached before three years of age.

The Ball Python has produced several color variations in captivity and more are to be expected. There is a concerted effort to selectively breed more contrastingly colored animals and those with regular pattern features, especially an even middorsal dark stripe. Albinos still are uncommon and very expensive, as are piebalds that have a normally colored head and tail but otherwise are white with one or two oval patches of normal pattern that may appear to be striped. Specimens with broad pale golden middorsal stripes occasionally appear. There is a strong possibility that the pale striped form is not genetic but instead is produced as a result of abnormally low incubation temperatures. This also may be true for piebalds (though piebald x piebald crosses recently have produced piebalds) and for the overall very pale tan and gold (caramel) specimens occasionally seen. Very dull axanthic specimens also are bred. Small clutch sizes prevent mass-

The head pattern of Ball Pythons is fairly distinctive. Photo by I. Francais.

production of color varieties in this species.

Taxonomic History

This species first was described by Shaw in 1802 in his *General Zoology*, 3: 347. It was known for many years before this, however, and the name actually is based on plates from Seba's earlier encyclopedia. Rather amazingly, this species has garnered only one synonym in almost 200 years, *Python belli* of Gray, 1842 (*Zool. Misc.*: 44), described from the Gambia. Its range is small for an African python, but it does not appear to be uniformly distributed over central Africa, avoiding densely forested areas. It is closely related to *Python anchietae* from south of its range, and it also has been suggested that it or a similar extinct species may be the remote ancestor of *Calabaria*. *P. regius* belongs to the *molurus*-group.

PYTHON RETICULATUS
Reticulated Python

This is the largest, or at least longest python, one of the most beautifully colored, and one of the most feared. The Retic is notorious as an aggressive biter that often never tames. Though hatchlings and young specimens may have decent personalities, adulthood almost always brings with it an awful personality.

Description

A rather slender python with a large, flattened head that is very distinct from the neck. The tail often is 13 to 14% of the total

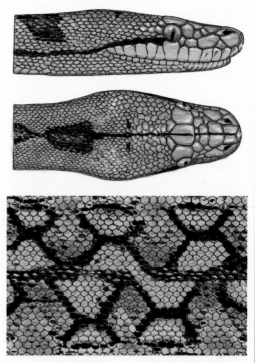

Head and midbody views of *P. reticulatus*.

length. The protuberant eyes are bright yellow to golden orange.

From above, the snout is rounded and the head appears somewhat elongated. The nostrils are lateral in position but visible from above, and the nasal scale almost is split into two. The rostral scale is barely visible from above, and there is a pair of large, somewhat squarish internasals. The anterior prefrontals are large and higher than wide. They are followed by a band of irregular scales that probably represent the posterior prefrontals. The frontal shield itself is large and rather oval in shape, often split into two by a vertical suture and sometimes fragmented posteriorly. The supraocular is large and usually undivided. The parietals are greatly fragmented. From the

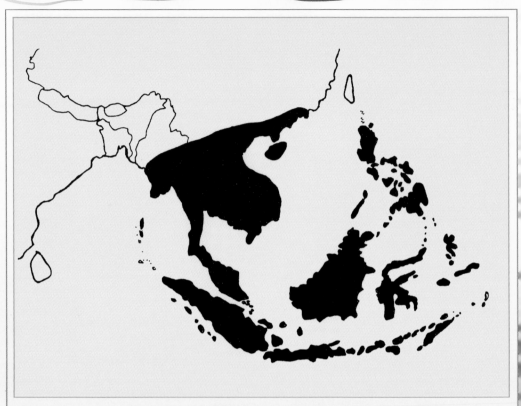

Above: Map of Southeast Asia and Indonesia showing the general natural distribution of *P. reticulatus. Below:* The diagonal labial pits of *P. reticulatus* show its close relationship to the Scrub and Carpet Pythons to the east. Photo by D. Dube.

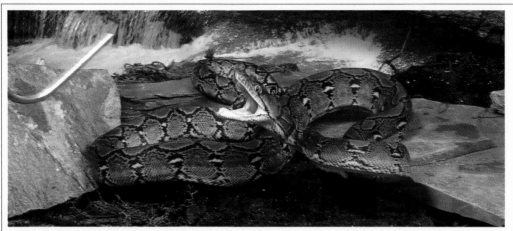

This juvenile Reticulated Python is demonstrating the aggressiveness this species is noted for. Even docile juveniles tend to become vicious in adulthood. Photo by I. Francais.

sides, the large nasal scale (or scales) is separated from the eye by two to four large, irregular, loreal scales and two preoculars of different sizes (the lower preocular small and sometimes broken). There are two to four small and irregular postoculars. The supralabials number from 10 to 14, the first four deeply pitted with rather narrow oblique slits. Usually only the seventh supralabial enters the eye. There are 20 to 23 infralabials, the anterior ones very narrow and elongated, six of the posterior ones with shallow rounded pits in a groove.

The scales are in 69 to 79 rows at midbody. There are 297 to 330 ventrals and 78 to 102 pairs of subcaudals.

The hemipenes are distinctly bilobed, the lobes ending in awns. The sulcus is bifurcate. There are three flounces. Males probe nine or ten subcaudals. It should be noted that the hemipenes of *P. reticulatus* resemble those of the Australian species more closely than the other Asian and African pythons. It also shares with the Australian species the slit-like pits on the anterior supralabials rather than the squarish pits of the African and other Asian species.

Most Retics are pale tan to yellowish, the color brighter anteriorly than posteriorly. The head is very cleanly colored, brown to bright yellow, with a narrow black stripe running straight from the nape to the tip of the snout, occasionally with short "horns" projecting to its sides at the back of the head. There is a narrow black stripe running obliquely from the back of the eye to the angle of the jaws. The body has a regular pattern of narrow dark brown saddles outlined with black isolating rounded to diamond-shaped areas of yellowish background color. On the sides the brown saddles alternate with oval whitish lozenges outlined with black. In juveniles the pattern, especially of the sides, is very clean-cut and

Retics are being bred in fair numbers. There are a few established pattern and color morphs; this is a striped Retic. Photo by R. D. Bartlett.

bright, but it becomes muddier and less distinct with growth. Often the yellowish diamonds or ovals down the middle of the back contain a central brown spot. In many specimens the brown saddles are themselves variably reticulated with dark and light brown scales. The belly is yellowish, speckled with black.

Typical adults are 5 or 6 meters long, with rare individuals exceeding 8 meters and at least one or two believable records of over 9.4 meters, and one of 10 meters (33 feet). Scattered weight records include 45 kilos at 4.3 meters, 82 kilos at 5.5 meters, and 145 kilos at 8.7 meters. Wild specimens are thought to grow about 0.75 to 1 meter per year for the first four or five years, but then slow considerably.

Natural Variation

Other than differences in head coloration and development of the diamonds on the back, this species seems to show little consistent variation. Subspecies have never been defined in the Retic, but there are suggestions that the brightness of the color may somehow be related to geography. As usual with large snakes, relatively few specimens are preserved in collections and there has been no detailed study of variation over the range of the species.

Natural History

The Reticulated Python is, like most other pythons, most common near large bodies of water. It hides by day and comes out to feed at dusk and dawn. A good climber, it is at home on stout branches in jungle trees, but it more commonly is seen near lakes, rivers, and canals, including those that are in crowded human cities. The range extends from southern Burma through southern China (including Hainan) over the entirety of Southeast Asia. The species continues through the Asian islands, including Sumatra, the Philippines, Sulawesi (Celebes), and Borneo, as well as most of the small islands in the area, eastward to Timor and the Flores. Reticulated Pythons are quite at home in the sea and have been reported moving between islands on many occasions. Old records from New Guinea are children. It is an extremely powerful constrictor that definitely has been seen to kill, but not eat, adult humans. It certainly can swallow dogs and cats and reportedly will take pigs as well, but most specimens prefer smaller prey that takes less effort to overcome.

Females in nature lay large clutches of eggs, reportedly as many as 100 but sometimes fewer than 20, which they guard. They do not seem to shiver to maintain

Uncommon in other species of pythons, Reticulated Pythons always have yellow-brown to bright orange eyes. Albino Retics have red eyes, of course. Photo by Z. Takacs

considered to be in error. This is a species of continually warm, humid areas, but it is quite tolerant of limited periods of cooler or drier weather.

Its large size enables it to feed on most mammals and birds in its range, and it has been repeatedly charged with killing and eating a higher temperature around the clutch. Hatchlings 600 to 750mm long emerge after 60 to 80 days of incubation.

This is one of the most persecuted snakes of southern Asia, as it is valued for both its skin and gall bladder. Many gravid females are collected for

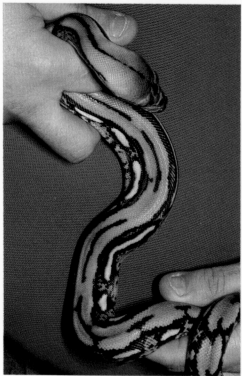

A newly developed morph is the tiger Retic, in which the diamonds across the back are reduced to a broken line. This morph is reported to be docile. Photo by M. Walls.

the market, held until they lay their eggs (which are hatched in captivity), and then killed for their skins and medicinally valuable internal organs.

Husbandry

Though Reticulated Pythons long have been common snakes in the terrarium, their large size and often ferocious attitudes have limited their popularity. The teeth of Retics are long, they are powerful constrictors, and bites often take weeks or months to heal unless antibiotics are used. These snakes are not for beginners, no matter how attractive and docile a young specimen may appear. Caution and forethought are advised.

Reticulated Pythons are large snakes (commonly adults exceed 6 meters in length), but spend the day coiled in the corner of the terrarium sleeping and thus do not need a tremendously large cage. Because hatchlings may grow almost a full meter each year for the first three or four years, they need a sufficiently large cage right from the start. A large water bowl is necessary as this is in many ways a distinctly aquatic species.

Rodents, chickens, guinea pigs, rabbits, and other similar mammals and birds form the usual foods. Do not try to get your specimen to take prey that is too large and requires too much exertion to swallow. Most Retics will take dead prey. A large Retic may be very expensive to feed. They usually digest their food in about four to ten days and then pass a large and messy fecal mass in their water bowl. Hatchlings may not feed for several weeks after they emerge, apparently without any harm. Feed in the evening for best results, but most captives feed readily at any time of the day.

Males have larger spurs than females, and they may fight if two males are penned together. They do not have to be over-wintered at lowered temperatures to breed. Eggs tend to be laid during the winter. They are the size of grapefruits and may number in the dozens. Females brooding eggs may be extremely aggressive, even compared to other

A very rare and expensive snake, this a gorgeous amelanistic (albino) Reticulated Python. A few breeders are working with these animals, so, in the future, they may be more readily available. Photo by W. P. Mara.

specimens of this normally aggressive species. The eggs hatch in about 80 days in captivity at 32°C (90°F). Hatchlings commonly are 700 to 900mm long in captive-breds and may grow to 3 meters during their first year of life. They may take several weeks before undergoing the first molt and then feeding.

Sexual maturity is reached in three to five years at lengths of 5 to 6 meters, females maturing more slowly and at a larger size than males. Adults may live well over 20 years in captivity.

Because of their large size, it is difficult to the average hobbyist to put together a colony for breeding purposes, but more and more captive-bred young are seen on the market. Especially favored are specimens with bright colors, including yellow heads and anterior bodies. Apparently some breeders are attempting to selectively breed for bright colors, but it is hard to tell whether the attempts are proving out as yet. Albinos have been recorded in nature but are rare and apparently not yet bred in captivity in commercial numbers. A new variant, the tiger Retic, has the pattern mostly restricted to the sides except for thin dark stripes down the back; it is said to be a dominant mutation. A few leucistics are known, and a heavily pale-spotted "calico" mutant now is being bred. Other mutations are known, but all variations from the typical pattern are rare.

Taxonomic History

In 1801 Schneider (*Hist. Amph.*, 2: 264) described *Boa reticulata*, and a few pages later he described *B. rhombeata*, now considered to be a synonym. Shaw, in his *General Zool.*, volume 3 (1802), described *Boa phrygia* and *Coluber javanicus* from the East Indies and Java, respectively. All presently are considered synonyms of *Python reticulatus.* The relationships of the Reticulated Python seem to be more with the New Guinea—Australian pythons commonly called *Morelia* than the species of the *molurus* group, and if *Python* is split it would seem to me that *reticulatus* should go into *Morelia* rather than *Python.*

PYTHON SEBAE
African Rock Python
The largest African python is the African Rock, which bears a striking similarity to the Asian Rock Python, *P. molurus*. It also is closely related to the Lesser Rock

---

Head and midbody views of *P. sebae.*

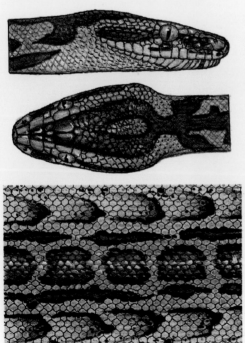

Python, *P. natalensis*, which here is recognized as a full species. This is one of the rarely available species that remains poorly known in captivity.

Description
The African Rock is a heavy-bodied cylindrical python with a large head distinct from the neck. The tail is about 11 to 12% of the total length. The scales on top of the head are large, and there is a distinctive head pattern. The eyes are small and very dark.

From above, the snout is narrowly rounded and the rostral scale is visible. The nostrils are just visible, and the nasals are separated by a pair of squarish internasals. The anterior prefrontals are large and well defined, followed by a band of a few irregular scales that separate them from the frontal, which commonly is split into equal halves by a vertical seam anteriorly and then developed as a rounded fragmented plate comprising several unequal scales. The supraocular is large and may be complete or split into two scales. From the side, the large nasal is separated from the eye by at least three or four loreals of various sizes and two preoculars, the lower one small and irregular. There are two to four postoculars. The supralabials number 13 to 16, numbers two and three rather shallowly pitted. There are 19 to 25 infralabials, the anterior ones very narrow; shallow pits occur on three anterior infralabials and three or four posterior ones.

The midbody scales are in 76 to 98 rows and there are 265 to 283 ventrals and 62 to 76 pairs of subcaudals. The anal scute may be entire or divided, and often there are many undivided subcaudals present.

The hemipenes are heavy and bilobed with awns at the tips of the lobes. There is a strong flounce on the stem. The sulcus is bifurcate beyond half the length of the organ.

The general coloration and body pattern resemble the Asian Rock Python. The background color of grayish to tan is marked with large irregular saddles of bright dark brown with black edges. The saddles are variable in shape and size and commonly fuse with the smaller alternating row of brown spots on each side. The top of the tail has a pale brown stripe edged by a dark line on each side.

From above, the head is dark brown, a continuation of the dark stripe on the nape. Often the center of the head is distinctly paler brown, dividing the brown patch into two broad bands or a Y that converges on the snout. A pale stripe runs from over the nostril over the top of the eye to

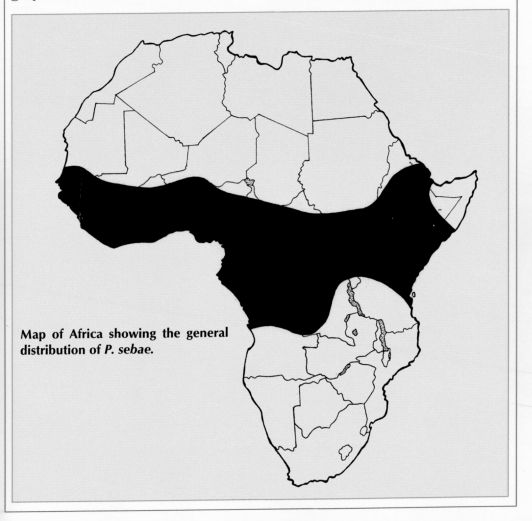

Map of Africa showing the general distribution of *P. sebae*.

Head scalation helps to distinguish *P. sebae* from *P. natalensis*. *P. sebae* has well developed shields when compared to the fragmented scales of *P. natalensis*. Photo by M. Walls. Courtesy of S. and R. Mitchell.

the back of the head and continues onto the body. From the side, the face is almost all dark brown except for two triangular whitish spots below the eye surrounding an oblique dark brown triangle. The band leading back from the eye is broad posteriorly, usually much wider than the eye diameter. The lower lip often is strongly spotted with dark brown. The belly is grayish to yellowish with black blotches.

This is a large python, one of the largest. Typical specimens are 4 to 6 meters long, with an apparently authentic record of an Ivory Coast specimen measuring 9.8 meters (32 feet) long.

Natural Variation

No subspecies are recognized because *natalensis*, long considered a synonym or subspecies, is recognized as a full species.

Natural History

Python sebae inhabits moist savannas and open forested areas at the edges of grasslands from Senegal to northern Angola in western Africa across central Africa south of the Sahara to Ethiopia, Somalia, and Kenya and Tanzania, including northern Zaire and Uganda. It may be quite common in populated areas and wherever there is standing water.

It climbs well and takes many types of mammalian and bird prey, including monkeys and small pigs as well as dogs. The snakes often lie in the shallows of lakes and canals waiting prey or hang from branches near water and grab prey animals as they pass by. They are strong constrictors, have large front teeth, and are vicious biters.

The eggs are laid in burrows by females during the wet season and commonly are 90 X 60mm. A hundred eggs may be laid in one clutch and guarded by the female, which does not shiver to increase the temperature. Incubation takes about two months.

Little is known of the status of this species in much of Africa, but it can be assumed that such a large snake will not survive for long in the present economic conditions in Africa. A good part of the range of this species has been struck by severe droughts, and food long has been at a premium. Typically pythons are not part of the diet in African countries, but I am sure that in extremis food is food. Few specimens are taken for the pet market and the skin market is not yet large in Africa.

Husbandry

African Rock Pythons are not common in captivity, perhaps because of their large size, bad tempers, and general resemblance to the much calmer *P. molurus*. The species can be kept much like any other large python, remembering that some specimens never tame down and

P. sebae is not common in the hobby market, but it does occasionally show up. Hatchlings generally are not expensive to buy, but remember that the adults are true giants that will be expensive to feed. Photo by W. P. Mara.

may spend much of their time attacking passing people and even pets through the glass and mesh of the cage. They are considered to be good feeders. If you keep them like Reticulated Pythons and take the same precautions you should be alright. The animals can be kept warm and humid all year. Be sure they have a large water bowl, some climbing branches, and a warm corner in which to spend the day.

as much as 10 kilos per year, and seem to reach maturity at an age of three years.

Too few animals have been produced in captivity to yield color varieties, but albinos can be expected shortly if they have not yet been produced. There presently is little demand for this species, which has all the problems associated with Reticulated Pythons but none of the colors.

In nature, African Rock Pythons inhabit savannas and forest-edges. Like other large pythons, adults live in and near bodies of standing water. Photo by P. Freed.

Breeding does not require a cool over-wintering period, but apparently one does not hurt and may make breeding easier. There are few captive breeding records for *Python sebae*. Eggs have been laid in February, hatching in as little as 52 and as many as 79 days. The young are about 550mm long. They grow rapidly for their first two or three years,

Taxonomic History

Like most large pythons, this species was known to the early naturalists and featured in the early encyclopedias such as Seba's *Thesaurus*. The plate in Seba served as the source of information for Gmelin's first (1789) description of this python in *Systema Naturae*, edition 13, 1: 1118. The Seba plate displayed an animal said to be from America, a common mistake of the time. Other early synonyms include *speciosus* Bonnaterre, 1789; *hieroglyphica* Schneider, 1801; *houttuyni* Daudin, 1803; *variegatus* Gray, 1842; and *liberiensis* Hallowell, 1845, all believed to be synonyms of *sebae* rather than *natalensis*, though the status of some of the early names remains unclear. Broadley, 1984, first clearly reviewed the structure of *P. sebae* and distinguished it from *P. natalensis* at the subspecific level.

PYTHON SPILOTUS
Common Carpet Python

The Common Carpet Python, here restricted to exclude the population from southwestern Australia known as *P. imbricatus*, is the current fad python in the North American terrarium hobby. Hobbyists spend large sums of money on bright black and yellow specimens, the so-called jungle phase, but this is an extremely variable species that still is not completely understood.

Description

Common Carpet Pythons are rather slender, cylindrical pythons, somewhat ridge-backed in young, with a broad head that is distinct from the slender neck. Only internasals and prefrontals are distinct on top of the head. The tail is about 12% of the total length, and the eye is dark olive in adults.

From above, the snout is broad and rounded, the nostrils large and barely visible. The rostral scale has the usual two deep pits

A most unusual snake, this is a partially striped Rock Python. Striping frequently is not genetic but instead is caused by cool temperatures during incubation. Photo by R. D. Bartlett.

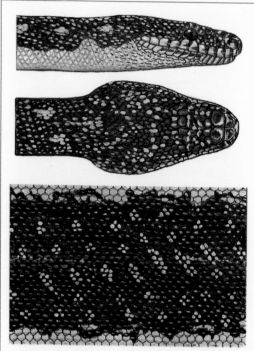

Head and midbody views of *P. spilotus*.

surrounding the eye, including two supralabials entering the lower edge of the eye. There are 11 to 14 supralabials, the first two deeply pitted and sometimes with a shallow pit or dimple on the third. The infralabials number about 17 to 20, the anterior ones narrow and strap-like, the posterior ones squarish and with about six to eight bearing deep pits in a groove.

The dorsal scales usually are in 45 to 51 rows (rarely to 64) at midbody; there commonly are 40 to 45 scales one head length behind the head and 27 to 30 one head length in front of the vent. Rarely a few scales at the posterior end of the body bear shallow pits, an exception in the genus. There are 251 to 310

and is visible from above. The internasals are of good size and squarish, sometimes with small scales partially separating them from each other or from the larger anterior prefrontals. There are one or two pairs of squarish prefrontals, the posterior pair often smaller and sometimes indistinct. The rest of the top of the head is covered with small and irregular scales, though sometimes a fairly distinct round frontal scale (often split) can be discerned; there are no obvious supraoculars (just small scales over the eyes) or parietals. From the side, the nasal is large and somewhat swollen. There are many (usually 20 or more) loreal scales of mixed sizes, three or four small preoculars, and five or so postoculars; there may be 10 to 12 or more small scales

Map of New Guinea showing the general distribution of *P. spilotus*.

Map of Australia showing the general natural range of *P. spilotus*.

ventrals and 63 to 94 pairs of subcaudals.

The hemipenis is shallowly forked, has a small awn at the end of each branch, and has a bifurcate sulcus. The male probes to nine or ten subcaudals.

The color and pattern of the Common Carpet Python vary considerably over its range, and two distinctive subspecies or groups of variants can be recognized. The southern form, the Diamond Python, is dark olive-green to almost black, each scale with a yellow center. In most populations some of the yellow spots merge to produce pairs of irregular small yellow spots along the middle of the back, each spot with a broken black outline. Commonly there also are vague broken yellow stripes or a series of spots low on the sides as well. The head is blackish or dark olive-green with many small yellow spots over the top, heaviest posteriorly, the lips yellow with narrow vertical black barring; there may be indistinct traces of more solid dark (blackish) bars back from the eye to the angle of the jaws, above the eye to the back of the head, and across the back of the head. The belly is yellow with black mottling and blotches that are more prominent posteriorly. The hatchlings of the Diamond Python more closely resembles the adults and hatchlings of the next form, the true Carpet Python, in being reddish brown with yellowish spots in about six rows across the back, the spots variably fused.

The true Carpet Python of

Pure Diamond Pythons are beautiful animals that are rare in the American and European hobbies. Breeders working with these snakes are few and far between. Photo by K. H. Switak.

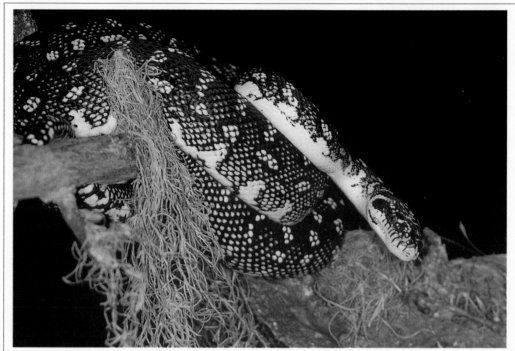

Including climbing branches in a Diamond or Carpet Python terrarium is a good idea, since these snakes are semi-arboreal in nature. Photo by P. Freed.

northeastern Australia and southeastern New Guinea tends to be a reddish brown snake with six rows of yellow spots across the back. These spots typically fuse into either complete yellowish bands isolating reddish brown bands or fuse partially to isolate irregular dark saddles over the midback and dark blotches low on the sides. Sometimes the yellow spots fuse to produce multiple yellow stripes over all or part of the body. In this subspecies the head pattern usually is very distinct and consists of a blackish stripe from the nostril through the eye to the angle of the jaws (often reduced anterior to the eye), a dark stripe from above the eye to the back of the head on each side, and often dark stripes across the head between the eyes, across the parietal region, and across the back of the head. Some specimens are contrastingly marked in black and yellow, others dull yellowish tan and indistinct reddish tan.

Typical adults of most populations are 2 meters or less in total length, but there are records of nearly 4 meters for the species.

Natural Variation

This may be one of the most variable of the pythons, though perhaps its current value in the hobby may be accentuating the importance of relatively minor variations. Though some herpetologists and hobbyists recognize as many as five subspecies in Australia plus at least one other in New Guinea, I feel the evidence for the reality of the subspecies (other than the Diamond Python) is weak at best. It seems that this is a species that has the ability to express an immense number of small differences in color pattern. When combined with a tendency for local populations to be incompletely isolated for at least short periods of time from their neighbors, you get the potential for literally dozens of weakly distinguishable color varieties over the range of the species in most of eastern Australia. I can find no good defining characters for the minor named variants other than trends in coloration that may not be fully linked with geography. I think it would be better if hobbyists who wished to recognize and trade in the minor variants used common names rather than perhaps meaningless subspecific names.

The two subspecies recognized here are the Diamond Python, *Python spilotus spilotus*, from the coastal forests of New South Wales, and the Carpet Python, *Python spilotus variegatus*, which ranges from eastern South Australia to Queensland and southeastern New Guinea, then west across northern Australia to northwestern Western Australia. These two subspecies correspond to the color descriptions given above. They seem to intergrade in northern New South Wales, and genetic influence of both color patterns extends many miles into the range of the other subspecies.

Recently hobbyists and others have given formal scientific names to a few of the many somewhat

This Carpet Python comes from Irian Jayan stock. The vast majority of Carpet Pythons for sale are Irian Jayan in origin, since this is the only government within their range that allows exportation. Photo by I. Francais.

distinctive color patterns within *P. s. variegatus*. These correspond to narrow and broad geographic forms, some of which have many other distinctive color forms within them. These minor forms include: the Coastal Carpet Python ["*mcdowelli*"] found in coastal wet forest from northern New South Wales to the Cape York Peninsula and southeastern New Guinea; the Jungle Carpet Python ["*cheynei*"] from the Atherton Tablelands of eastern central Queensland, a sometimes small yellow and black form that may co-occur with the Coastal form and also occurs in New

probably dozens of equally indistinct forms could be recognized if one were to examine the species in detail over its entire range. It should also be noted that few breeders agree on exactly what each minor form should look like, and there may be extensive variation in every individual specimen with age, the color going from brown to reddish brown to yellowish brown to yellow and black, back to reddish brown and finally dull brown as the snake ages.

Natural History

The Common Carpet Python ranges from southern and southeastern Australia north to northern Western Australia and the tip of Queensland and into southeastern New Guinea. The status of the New Guinea populations is poorly known, but the species seems to be a recent arrival on that island.

Although Carpet Pythons normally are docile, you should always exercise caution when handling large snakes. Photo by R. D. Bartlett.

Guinea; the Inland Carpet Python ["*metcalfei*"], an exceeding variable composite of forms that occupies a large area of interior eastern Australia from eastern South Australia to central Queensland in dry woodlands; and the Northwestern Carpet Python [*variegatus* in its restricted form], a nearly ringed snake found in dry woodlands from northern Western Australia to western Queensland. As mentioned,

This python occupies many different habitats over its large range, from dense rain forest to open scrub and river bottoms to sandstone cliffs. Typically Common Carpet Pythons are arboreal, but they also are active on the ground in many areas. Active mostly at night, some can also be found moving around during the day. They eat a broad range of mammals and birds, and young specimens seem to be lizard specialists. In other words, this is a very adaptable species that can be found almost anywhere and anytime within its range.

As far as is known, this is the only amelanistic Carpet Python in existence. It was found in the wild near Darwin, Australia. Photo by K. H. Switak.

Though in theory protected from export by Australian and Papuan laws, many specimens have reached the market in the last few years, most (of various color varieties) supposedly coming from Irian Jaya, where the species is very rare and almost certainly not available in commercial quantities.

This is an example of the inland Carpet Python, designated *P. spilotus "metcalfei"* in the hobby. The validity of most Carpet Python subspecies is questionable. Photo by K. H. Switak.

Husbandry

Carpet and Diamond Pythons are very aggressive pythons, and they should not be housed together. Males are especially likely to become involved in combat rituals that can lead to bloody bites. Care is much like that for any other large pythons. Give the snake a large terrarium that can be securely locked. Depending on the habitat from which your particular specimen came, a daytime temperature of about 28 to 30°C (82 to 86°F) or a bit higher, with a drop of a few degrees at night, will suffice. Specimens from wet coastal forests like it a bit cooler than those from dry inland open woodlands. Provide a basking temperature several degrees higher, as gravid females like to bask. Carpet Pythons like sturdy branches and a hide box in the terrarium to make them feel comfortable. Give them a water bowl and also spray the terrarium occasionally.

The jungle Carpet Python, *P. s. "cheynei"*, is quite an attractive animal clad in black and yellow. Unfortunately, most Carpet Pythons will change color over the course of their lives, often becoming duller. Photo by M. Burger.

Adults feed mostly on mammals and take rats, guinea pigs, gerbils, and occasionally larger prey such as rabbits. Some will take birds as well. Feeding in the evening when the snakes are most active is normal. Hatchlings and young specimens may refuse mice and feed only on large lizards such as skinks.

Few keepers have much luck breeding Carpet and Diamond Pythons, though more and more captive-breds are available each year. Many specimens still are wild-caught adults or captive-hatched young from gravid wild-caught females. Both sexes have a large spur on each side of the cloaca, but males have longer spurs that often have a small projection or claw near the base. Males will fight viciously when females are present.

Some keepers have had success by cooling their snakes to about 25°C (77°F) for two or three months while reducing the hours of daylight and cutting back on food. Other keepers feel that a cooling period is unnecessary.

Females lay clutches of about 15 to 40 eggs about 50mm long. They are laid in a tight, adhesive clump and brooded by the mother, who shivers to raise the temperature a few degrees. If the eggs are removed from the mother for incubation, they must be kept humid and at a temperature of about 32°C (90°F). The hatchlings emerge in eight to ten weeks and are about 400mm long. They may be difficult to start feeding on mice, and lizards may be necessary. Most start feeding after their first shed, which may be several weeks after hatching.

Intergrades between Diamond and Carpet Pythons occur in the wild on occasion and are captive bred in good numbers. Photo by I. Francais.

Hatchlings of most forms are reddish brown or brown, but the color and pattern almost always change every few months as the youngsters grow.

Many specimens on the market today seem to be crosses of Diamond Pythons with one or another color variety of Carpet Python. Such mixes almost certainly will not breed true, and when they are crossed with still other color varieties, who knows what you will get.

Taxonomic History

The Common Carpet Python has a long and complicated taxonomic history. The name *Python spilotus* (for the Diamond Python) goes back to Lacepede, 1804 (*Ann. Mus. Natl. Hist. Nat.*, 4: 194-195) and was based on a specimen from southeastern Australia. For many years the species was known as *argus* Linnaeus, 1758, but that name was based on a drawing in one of Seba's encyclopedias that either is unrecognizable or represents some type of colubrid with large plates on top of the head. *Morelia variegata* was described by Gray in 1842 (*Zool. Misc.*: 43) from a specimen from Port Essington in northern Australia. The names *peronii* Wagler, 1828, and *punctata* Gray, 1842, are synonyms of the Diamond Python. The minor color forms (*cheynei, mcdowelli, metcalfei*) were described by Wells and Wellington in their controversial *Australian J. Herpetology*, the first two names in 1984 and the third in 1985; *mcdowelli* and perhaps *cheynei* may be incorrectly formed.

PYTHON TIMORIENSIS
Timor Python

The Timor Python was described in an off-hand way over a hundred years ago and remains something of an enigma today. It is closely related to *P. amethistinus* but also shows many similarities to *P. reticulatus*, being one of the main reasons for synonymizing *Morelia* with *Python*. However, no one has ever examined a long series of Timors and the full range of variation in the species remains unknown.

Description

A large, cylindrical python with a wide, flattened head and a strong resemblance to a Reticulated or Scrub Python. The eyes are olive-gold.

From above, the snout is broadly rounded and the nostrils are visible in large nasal shields.

Head and midbody views of *P. timoriensis*.

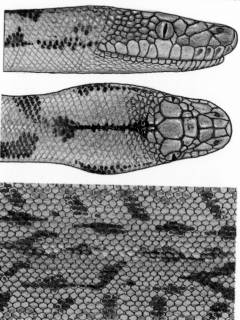

P. timoriensis is an odd snake that, structurally speaking, appears to be a stable population derived from hybrids of *P. amethistinus* and *P. reticulatus*. Photo by R. D. Bartlett.

There are two rather squarish internasals followed by a larger pair of anterior prefrontals that may be partially fused. There are two or four posterior prefrontals that are much smaller than the anterior prefrontals and in broad contact with the large oval to hexagonal frontal. The supraocular is large and undivided. There are two (Timor) or three (Flores) pairs of parietal scales that may be partially fused or irregularly broken. From the side, there are about six loreal scales of mixed sizes between the nasal and the prefrontals. The two prefrontals are of different sizes, the upper much larger than the lower. There are three to four postoculars of uneven sizes. The supralabials number 11 or 12, of which one enters the lower border of the eye, and the first four supralabials are deeply and obliquely pitted. The 16 or 17

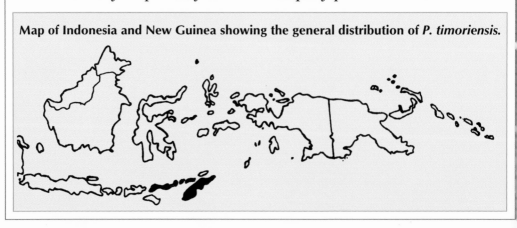

Map of Indonesia and New Guinea showing the general distribution of *P. timoriensis*.

infralabials are narrow anteriorly and squarish posteriorly, with four or five posterior scales bearing pits in a groove.

The dorsal scales are in about 60 to 63 rows at midbody, 55 one head length behind the head, and 33 one head length before the vent. The ventrals number 287 or 288, the subcaudals are unknown because the reported specimens also may be some dark outlining of the main head shields. The color pattern seems to be variable but generally consists of a network of dark brown lines across the back and along the sides, outlining rounded to vaguely diamond-shaped clear areas of background color. The bars on the side often are vertical and may fuse into a broken stripe

Despite being closely related to the giant Scrub and Reticulated Pythons, Timor Pythons generally stay smaller, rarely reaching more than 3 meters/ 10.5 feet. Photo by P. Freed.

have broken tails; a much wider variation in ventral counts should be expected.

Males probe about 15 subcaudals.

The general body color is pale tan to light olive-brown, the belly yellowish. The head is unpatterned except for a narrow dark stripe extending from the nape down the center of the head to about between the eyes; there just above the ventrals.

Most specimens seen have been 1 to 3 meters in length.

Natural Variation

There is considerable variation in the development of the posterior prefrontals, whether two or four, and in the degree of fusion or splitting of the anterior prefrontals and the parietals. There are indications that specimens from the Flores may be distinct from those collected in Timor.

Natural History

The Timor Python is known from Timor and the Flores Islands in eastern Indonesia west of New Guinea. It appears to be uncommon to rare, but this may be caused by confusion with the similar Reticulated Python, which also occurs in these islands. The Scrub Python occurs just one island group to the east but does not appear to co-exist with the Timor Python.

As far as known, the species occurs in wooded areas near water, much like the other large pythons. Its home area is continually hot and humid. It feeds on mammals and probably on birds.

Only a few specimens are collected for the terrarium market.

Husbandry

There is little hobby experience with this rare python, but it should be kept much like the Scrub Python, given a cage of large size and securely latched. If kept at about 30°C (86°F), a bit cooler at night, and given a warmer basking area, it should do well. It needs sturdy climbing branches, a hide box in which to spend the day, and a large water bowl. Timor Pythons are active mostly at night and take the usual array of rats, guinea pigs, chickens, and rabbits as food.

Little has been reported on captive breeding of the Timor Python, but the eggs have been laid in April and hatched in July after 60 to 80 days at about 32°C (90°F). The young are some 300 to 400mm long and will take mice after their first shed.

Due to its remote habitat and general rarity, the Timor Python is somewhat mysterious. Little is known about its behavior and natural history. Photo by P. Freed.

black; there may be a distinct dark-lined head pattern much like that of a Common Carpet Python and a dark brown or nearly black line down the middle of the back. Many hatchlings have bright yellow tail tips that may be used for luring prey into striking range.

Most adult Green Tree Pythons are about 1.5 to 1.8 meters in length. The record appears to be about 2.2 meters. Males are shorter and lighter in build than females.

Natural Variation

Though simply colored and patterned, Green Tree Pythons show quite a bit of apparently individual variation. The lips may be green or whitish rather than yellow, and some specimens have so much yellow on the body that they appear to be covered with irregular yellow and green stripes. The development of white spotting varies considerably from just a few specks scattered at random to a distinctly and regularly spotted pattern down the center of the back, the spots connected by a distinct pale stripe. Many specimens have a distinct blue tinge, especially prominent along the middorsal area, and apparently this character can be selected for and may be genetic. A few specimens lack the yellow

entirely (axanthics), being bright blue above and white below. It is reported that old females may lose much of their green color and turn bluish.

Hatchlings are shades of red or bright yellow with well-developed white spots and head markings. Some juveniles bear a distinct resemblance to Common Carpet Pythons, especially when the head pattern is strongly developed. Most juveniles begin to turn green

This yellow juvenile is about five months old. It should start changing color within the next month or so of its life. Photo by K. H. Switak.

between three and six months of age, but adults often retain some aspects of the juvenile pattern, especially yellow spotting and blotches.

There seems to be little evidence that color variation and differences in the scale counts are strongly correlated with geography, and no one has ever attempted to describe subspecies in this species.

Natural History

Python viridis is a species of dense to open forests throughout the islands of New Guinea, including Misool and Salawati to the west and the Aru Islands to the south. It also occurs in coastal rain forest along the northeastern coast of Queensland, Australia. The snakes spend the day quietly coiled, hanging from branches in the trees. The coil shape is planar, with the head in the center, a distinctive behavior shared with the externally similar Emerald Tree Boa (*Corallus caninus*) of tropical America. At night they descend to the ground and actively search for mammals of all types, especially native rats. Both juveniles and adults have been noted to twitch the tail tip to attract prey, both lizards and mammals. Though it long has been stated that the enlarged anterior teeth are an adaptation for grabbing birds and penetrating their feathers, stomach contents of wild specimens contain only mammals, not birds. Juveniles appear to specialize on lizards as their diet, perhaps thus avoiding competition with adults for food. Some adults in nature still take lizards, however.

The forests of New Guinea vary considerably in their humidity and temperature, but as a rule (especially for those accessible enough to allow Green Tree Pythons to be collected) they are warm, 32°C (90°F), and have an almost saturated humidity during the wet season for six months. During the six months of dry season the temperature may be almost 20 degrees cooler (especially at night) and the humidity may be only 60%. The pythons often are able to drink by sucking droplets of water off their coils.

Green Tree Pythons have a bad reputation in the literature, being considered hard to handle and quick to strike. Experienced keepers, however, often feel that they simply are misunderstood,

The nasal scales of Green Tree Pythons grow large and bulbous, giving the snout an almost squarish appearance. Photo by K. H. Switak.

Above: A normal Green Tree Python resting in their typical resting position. The only other snake that regularly coils in this fashion is the Emerald Tree Boa, a remarkably similar animal. *Below:* Blue *P. viridis* are uncommon and highly sought after animals. Sometimes, normal green animals will turn blue as they age, usually retaining green on the head. Photos by R. D. Bartlett.

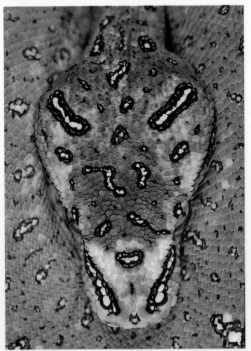

This is a *P. viridis* in the process of changing green. This occurs gradually, over a few months. Photo by K. H. Switak.

being quick to strike but not necessarily mean. Regardless, their large teeth and strong bites can result in deep, painful bites, especially if they hit the face. Caution is advised.

Though apparently common in parts of New Guinea, many specimens still are taken for export for the pet market, though captive-bred specimens finally may be driving out this trade. Wild-caught adults may be heavily parasitized and slow to adapt to foods offered in captivity. The species also is considered quite edible and is hunted for the pot.

Husbandry

The cages for Green Tree Pythons must reflect their natural arboreal behavior. Commonly the pythons are housed in large vertical terraria with glass fronts and several wooden dowel perches staggered across the cage at various levels. The dowels should be of a diameter appropriate to the size of the snake, about 35mm for adults. Hide boxes, either empty or partially filled with damp sphagnum, are hung from the sides of the cage. The terrarium can be misted two or more times a day using a spray bottle or an automatic misting system, or a water bowl in the bottom of the cage can be fitted with a pump and air stone to produce a fine spray of water. Humidity should be about 70 to 80% most of the time, increased to about 100% when the pythons are ready to shed.

Most captive-bred *P. viridis* will take mice and rats of appropriate size, but some young may require ground skinks (*Scincella*) or geckos as an early food. Remember that Greenies may strike before they think; use forceps when feeding and watch your hands and face.

Captives have been known to live for over 20 years, and they may become sexually mature in under two years. Unlike most pythons, in which the males has spurs that are slightly and sometimes not visually larger than those of the female, the spurs of males Green Pythons are very large compared to those of the females.

Most luck in breeding Green Tree Pythons has come from cooling them to about 21°C (70°F) in October and also reducing the humidity (to about 60%) and shortening the day length. After one or two months the temperature is raised to about 27°C (81°F). Because two males may have bloody fights, the typical colony consists of one adult male and two or three females. Mating occurs on a perch or sometimes in a hide box (especially if the latter has plenty of damp sphagnum moss). From six to 30 eggs are laid some two months after mating. The eggs can be left in the care of the mother or removed to an incubator with fairly dry vermiculite or a similar substrate. They hatch after 45 to 50 days at about 32°C (90°F). The young are about 280 to 350mm in length.

The change from the juvenile yellow or red coloration may occur very quickly (over just a few days) or may take years. As a rule, fast-growing juveniles change faster than do poor feeders, and yellows change faster than reds.

Currently many hobbyists like the blue phases of *P. viridis*, and some breeders are trying, with varying results, to selectively breed for blue. Unfortunately, there still is no strong evidence that blue coloration is genetic, and it is reported that a green specimen can change to bluish late in life. True blue mutations, axanthics (lacking yellow, the normal green coloration being due to an overlay of blue pigments by yellow in the skin), are rare and virtually unavailable.

One way to tell the Green Tree Python from the Emerald Tree Boa is to look at the head scales. Emerald Tree Boas have large shields, while the pythons have granular scales down to the nasals. Photo by K. H. Switak.

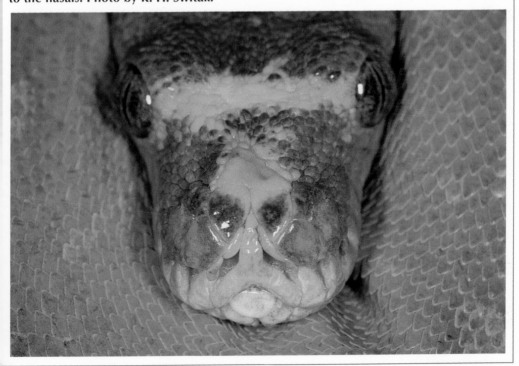

Frequently different colors of young will hatch out from the same clutch. These Green Tree Python babies are siblings from one clutch. Photo by K. H. Switak.

If at all possible, only captive-bred juveniles, regardless of color, should be purchased if you want an adaptable, long-lived pet. The price and availability of captive-breds have become much more reasonable in recent years, and some breeders now can mass-produce babies in a limited way. These are truly beautiful snakes with many admirers.

Taxonomic History

Python viridis was first described by Schlegel in 1872 (*Dierentuin Gen. Nat. Amst., Rept.*: 54) in a fast and dirty but valid description; his type came from the Aru Islands south of New Guinea. In 1875, Meyer (*Monataber. Preuss. Akad. Wiss. Berlin*, 1874: 134) described *Chondropython azureus* as a new genus and species from Mysore, now known as Biak Island, and in 1878 Sauvage (*Bull. Soc. Philomath. Paris*, (7) 2: 37) described *Chondropython pulcher* from Manokwari Island. The species has so far acquired no other synonyms. *Chondropython* first went into synonymy (with *Morelia*) in Wells and Wellington, 1984.

pythons (*Aspidites*) also lacks premaxillary teeth, while some specimens of *Python viridis* also lack them, but no known true python family (including Pythonidae, Calabariidae, and Loxocemidae) lacks the postfrontal bone. The postfrontal of *Calabaria* fails to contact the prefrontal (it makes contact in Loxocemidae and Pythonidae), perhaps as a

There are on average 18 maxillary teeth, no palatine teeth and no pterygoid teeth (i.e., there are no teeth on the roof of the mouth), and about 18 dentary (mandibular) teeth. The coronoid bone is large.

Adults typically are 60 to 80 cm in total length, with the record at about one meter. The tail is only 7 to 8% of the total length.

This individual is nearly ready to shed its skin. Like other snakes, Calabar Pythons turn dull and acquire a bluish cast to their skin when they are about to shed. Photo by K. H. Switak.

function of the arching of the skull over the orbit. Many details of the skull and jaw structure are similar to those of Pythonidae, and some are especially similar to the condition in *Python* itself. For a discussion of these similarities, see McDowell, 1975. The entire skull appears very compact, with the anterior portion especially solid, an obvious adaptation for burrowing. The teeth are large and heavy in the Calabar Python.

Natural Variation

Though there are no recent studies of variation in the species, there is no indication in the literature that subspecies could be recognized or a cryptic species is lying hidden in *Calabaria reinhardti*. The variation in color and pattern seems to be individual.

Natural History

Calabar was a region on the

western coast of Africa during the days of the slave trade and the later European partitioning of Africa (today part of southern Nigeria). The species ranges over West Africa from Liberia to the Ituri Forest of Zaire. Much of this area is typical low, hot, humid African coastal forest, but the species also occurs at the edges of savannas and in populated areas. It is strongly associated with termite mounds and in nature termites may form a good portion of its diet, at least when young. The eggs in nature may be laid in and near termite mounds as well. In many areas the snakes are found under logs and piles of leaves and other detritus in burrows several centimeters below the surface.

Adults eat a variety of foods, from small mice to earthworms. They are not constrictors in the typical sense, often using their strong coils to press prey against the walls of a burrow. Unlike many burrowing snakes, Calabar Pythons are active not only at night but often in the morning and evening as well (crepuscular), and they often are found crossing roads on dull days. There are persistent reports of this species being found a few meters above the ground in shrubs and also in termite mounds, and it definitely can climb well. Like other small burrowers, *Calabaria* are very gentle and have a reputation for never biting (though their teeth are large enough to inflict some damage). They are a typical balling snake, keeping the head hidden under a ball of coils while the tail extends outward and up to attract attention.

Virtually nothing is reported about reproduction in the wild, and we'll discuss what is known later under Husbandry. Like most tropical pythons, the eggs probably are laid during the local dry season and the young hatch near the beginning of the rainy season when many food animals become available. It has been suggested that in nature the female guards and perhaps incubates her eggs, but I know of no confirmation of this. Indications are that eggs taken from wild-caught females laying in captivity in Africa almost always fungus shortly after being taken from the mother, a hint that maternal care may occur.

Calabar Pythons are common and sometimes abundant animals in western Africa. Occasional specimens are exported for the pet trade, but the animal cannot be said to be common in the hobby. Many are shipped through Senegal and other countries where they do not occur, the specimens being illegally collected in Zaire and other areas and then transshipped through countries that have no restrictions on their export. It is unfortunate that hobbyists so far have had little luck breeding this species.

Husbandry

A 20-gallon-long terrarium with a sturdy locking mesh lid provides a good home for one or two Calabar Pythons. The substrate should be 100 to 150mm of a peat moss, sand, and loam mixture topped with another 25mm or so of leaf mulch. There should be several tight-fitting hide boxes, pieces of cork bark, and a few sturdy branches for the occasional climb. An average temperature of 28 to 32°C (82-90°F), a bit lower at night, is adequate. A small undertank heating pad under one corner of the terrarium will help maintain suitable temperatures. Unlike many other burrowers, Calabars may be active during the day and occasionally will bask on a flat rock under a weak basking lamp. Other light sources are not necessary, though some hobbyists provide fluorescent lights for when the snake decides to become active. Provide a shallow water bowl (some specimens will bathe) and also spray the terrarium every few days to increase the humidity.

Feeding wild-caught specimens may be a problem, as many are stressed and parasitized and refuse to eat. Try small (fuzzy or hopper) mice placed in a small bag or box with the snake for a few hours. Give the specimen complete darkness and solitude and it might eat. Some young specimens will take earthworms and even termites. If you can get a specimen to eat it should live for several years, but admittedly most specimens die in a few months or a year.

The sexes are hard to tell apart, but males have obvious pointed spurs that may be hidden in females. If probed, the hemipene pouches of a male will extend for about ten subcaudal scales. There have been few successful captive breedings, though some clutches laid by gravid imports have been brought to hatching. Mating in nature seems to occur mostly in November or December, with the

This female laid these eggs shortly after capture. It is only very recently that true captive breeding of this species has occurred, so captive-bred specimens are still rare. Photo by K. H. Switak.

eggs laid about six months later, in April to June. The eggs are very large for a small snake (commonly 100mm long and 35mm in diameter) and only a few comprise a clutch, typically three or four. The eggs are very sensitive to fungal and bacterial infections and seldom survive for more than a few days or weeks. Incubation may be short, as little as six weeks.

If you can get your hands on a few specimens to establish a colony, you might want to try giving them an alternating dry and wet season cycle in an attempt to imitate natural conditions. You also might try letting females stay with their eggs if you should happen to get a clutch. What have you got to lose?

Taxonomic History

Except for a bit of confusion caused by nearly simultaneous descriptions of genera for the species described as *Eryx reinhardtii* by Schlegel in 1848 (*Bijdr. tot Dierk.*, 1: 2, type locality Gold Coast), the history of this species is rather simple. In 1858 Gray of the British Museum described the new genus and species *Calabaria fusca* from Calabar Coast, a synonym of Schlegel's species but a good new generic name. Later in the same year Peters erected the new genus *Rhoptrura* for Schlegel's *reinhardti*, not having seen Gray's new description. The synonymy was noticed in a few years and the combination *Calabaria reinhardti* has been accepted since at least 1893.

The relationships of the genus are still in question, however, as mentioned in the introduction. I feel that if interpreted strictly on the development of characters of the skull, *Calabaria* has many features indicating that it is related to the Pythonidae, and possibly to *Python* or an intermediate ancestor. These include features of the paroccipital process, basipterygoid process, Meckelian cartilage, palatine-pterygoid contact, postfrontal (supraorbital) bone, and jaw articulation, as delineated by McDowell (1975). Absence of premaxillary teeth, a boid character, also occurs in a typical python (*Aspidites*) and certainly is a loss related to burrowing adaptations. The vertebrae of the tail are fused in a way similar to erycid boas (*Charina, Eryx*), but again this probably is a parallel development and an adaptation for burrowing rather than a sign of relationships. The hemipenis is unique in form though it might possibly be derived from one similar to *Python*; regardless, it is no more similar to the hemipenes of erycid boas than to pythons. I can see no case for moving *Calabaria* into the erycid boas and certainly no case at all for synonymizing the genus with *Charina* as did Kluge in 1993. The combination of primitive and specialized characters indicates to me a primitive form that has been going its own way for many years and is no more closely related to the true pythons than to the boas, thus deserving its own family.

THE NEOTROPICAL PYTHONS, FAMILY LOXOCEMIDAE

I've often thought that these unusual American snakes should be called "Hognosed Pythons" on account of their most prominent feature: the enlarged, upturned rostral scale. Like many other primitive burrowers, they exhibit an array of characters that have made their classification at the family level difficult or impossible. In many aspects of their skull structure they are fairly typical pythons. They have been considered a subfamily of the python complex, a full family (as treated here), a part of the family Xenopeltidae allied to the Aniliidae rather than the pythons, and part of a strange family containing *Loxocemus, Xenopeltis*, and *Calabaria*, all the small burrowing python-like snakes. Their isolated range, specializations for burrowing, and similarities to so many other groups speak for them as being a relict of one of the ancestors of the more typical pythons, and I feel it is more meaningful to consider them a full family. There is only one genus and species, *Loxocemus bicolor*, presently recognized.

Genus *Loxocemus* Cope, 1862 (*Proc. Acad. Nat. Sci. Phila.*, 13: 77). Type species by monotypy *bicolor*.

Cylindrical snakes with 31 to 35 scale rows at midbody, moderately wide ventral scales, a short tail with subcaudals in two rows, and a distinct mental groove under the chin. The head is slightly widened but not distinct from the neck and has a

---

Head and midbody views of *L. bicolor*.

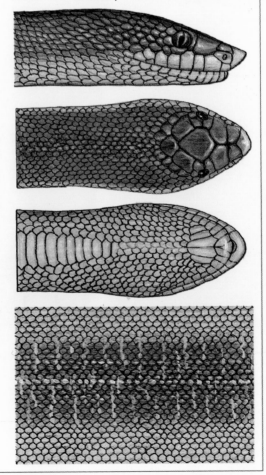

Map of Mexico showing general distribution of *L. bicolor.*

Map of Central America showing the general range of *L. bicolor.*

large, projecting rostral scale that is broadly wedge-shaped; the eyes are fairly large and have vertically elliptical pupils. The head shields are large and constant in shape and position, including a pair of internasals slightly separated by the rostral, a pair of rather strap-like prefrontals that extend ventrally to contact the supralabials, a large roundly triangular frontal, and several parietals; there is no loreal (with rare exceptions), and the number of scales about the eye varies within narrow limits. A single variable species is known.

LOXOCEMUS BICOLOR
Neotropical Python

This is a snake of many common names, including Mexican Burrowing Python, American Python, Burrowing Python, Dwarf Python, and varying combinations of these. I prefer the simpler Neotropical Python because it accurately refers to its range in Central America. Though not a colorful snake, it is occasionally available and easy to keep though almost impossible to breed in captivity so far.

Description

These odd pythons are rather cylindrical in shape and fairly heavy-bodied. Few specimens exceed a meter in length, and most are only 60 to 80 cm long. The head is large and not greatly flattened, ending in the large wedge-shaped and slightly upturned "hognose" rostral scale. The tail is fairly short and blunt, with paired subcaudal scales; the anal plate is split. The scales are polished and iridescent, though under magnification they bear 3 very fine tubercles or pits. The scales of the back are in 31 to 33 (rarely 35) rows at midbody, decreasing to 23 to 26 rows in front of the vent.

From above, the head is distinctly pointed and the rostral scale is long, wide, and partially separates the internasals, which are fairly large. The prefrontals are larger than the internasals and rather strap-like, extending down to touch the supralabials. There usually is a single supraocular. The frontal is large and roundly triangular or diamond-shaped. The parietals are small, and there is a small medial parietal scale (variable in shape and size, an azygous scale)

The upturned nose of the Neotropical Python is indicative of its burrowing habits. Photo by R. D. Bartlett.

at the tip of the frontal, dividing the parietals medially. From the side, the rostral is bluntly pointed and strongly projecting. The nostril is between two small scales, there is no loreal but the prefrontal is broadly visible (rarely a seam splits the prefrontal to produce an indistinct loreal), and there is a distinct preocular that occasionally splits into two; there are three or four postoculars. The supralabials are low and nearly square, about 9 to 11 in number; typically numbers 4 and 5 or 5 and 6 enter the eye from below, but occasionally a small subocular scale blocks them from the eye. There are 11 to 14 infralabials, usually two in contact with the single distinct pair of large gular scales. The eye is dark, with a vertical pupil.

The ventral and subcaudal scales vary geographically (a cline), with fewer in the northern part of the range than in the south. Over the entire range there are 234 to 270 ventrals and 39 to 52 pairs of subcaudals. In Honduran specimens these numbers are 252 to 267 and 46 to 50, respectively. The lowermost row of body scales is distinctly larger than the others.

The hemipenis is weakly but distinctly bilobed and has a bifurcate sulcus, each branch ending in a distinct smooth disk. There are several flounces from the middle of the shaft outward. The hemipenis is very similar to that of *Xenopeltis*. The left lung is large, about 78% the length of the right. The pelvis is represented by two bones and there is a distinct femur, so this snake is well-equipped with small but distinct spurs.

In color this is a very plain snake, being bluish brown to grayish brown above and on top of the head. Most specimens are quite iridescent. The belly varies greatly from uniformly grayish brown to bright yellow. If the belly is pale, the color extends up the side over the lowermost scale rows and the side of the face. In some specimens there are small pinkish to whitish dots scattered over the back, these sometimes forming larger spots but never a regular pattern.

The skull of the Neotropical Python in much like that of the true pythons. There is a postfrontal bone present at the back of the orbit. The premaxillaries are large and projecting (to support the burrowing snout), and they bear at least a pair of teeth. The anterior teeth in the upper and lower jaws are longer than the posterior ones. On average, there are about 20 maxillary teeth, 6 palatine teeth, 8 pterygoid teeth, and 18 dentary teeth. The lower jaw is about normal in shape for a python, and there is a distinct coronoid bone.

Adults typically are between 60 cm and a meter long, with the record apparently being a female from Oaxaca, Mexico, that was 1309mm long.

Natural Variation

The Neotropical Python long has confused taxonomists because it has two different

L. bicolor generally makes a nice, docile pet. Hopefully, they will become more available when the secrets of breeding them are unraveled. Photo by R. Kayne.

ventral colors. In most specimens the belly is white to yellow, but in many it is grayish brown, only slightly paler than the back. The type specimen of *L. bicolor* has a pale belly, as hinted by the scientific name. *Loxocemus sumichrasti* Bocourt, 1876, has a dark belly. *L. bicolor* was described from La Union, El Salvador, the southern part of the range, while *L. sumichrasti* came from Tehuantepec, in the northern part of the range. For many years specimens of these snakes were uncommonly collected, and it seemed as though two species or subspecies could be recognized, a northern dark-bellied form (*sumichrasti*) and a southern pale-bellied form (*bicolor*). The species now is collected in numbers from most of its range, and the last analysis of variation showed that there is no correlation between belly color and range or any other color or structural character and range. Both color forms can occur at one locality, and intermediate specimens (pale bellies with dark blotches; belly pale anteriorly becoming dark posteriorly) are known. There seems to be no basis to recognize subspecies in *L. bicolor*.

Natural History

The range of the Neotropical Python includes low-altitude dry forests, especially thorn scrub, from Nayarit, Mexico, southward to northwestern Costa Rica on the Pacific Coast. It also occurs on the

Atlantic slope of Chiapas, Mexico, and northern Honduras, but this is basically a snake of Pacific Central America.

Little is known about its natural history, and what is known is based mostly on random collections, especially of snakes taken along highways at night. It is largely nocturnal, hiding during the day under rock piles, logs, and other debris. According to some reports, it is more likely to be found under deep piles of leaves than actually burrowed into the soil. Newly hatched young have been found in May. Other reproductive information is discussed under Husbandry.

Loxocemus bicolor feeds on small mammals and possibly birds in nature. The few specimens I have handled were gentle and attempted to ball up when handled, but they can and sometimes do bite. They may be locally common but secretive and do not appear to be threatened by any factors other than loss of habitat in more populated areas. Unfortunately, arid coastal habitats in Central America make excellent areas for development of resorts.

Husbandry

If you remember that this is a nocturnal species from rather dry habitats, you should have no problem keeping the occasional Neotropical Python you might find at the pet shop. Give them a 20-gallon-long terrarium with a loose soil substrate at least 100mm deep. Be sure to mix the soil with sand and some peat so it stays loose. Spray the bottom twice a week to make sure it stays just a bit on the moist side of dry. A water bowl can be given but may not be used. Provide the snakes with several hide boxes, pieces of cork bark, and other hiding places. They do well at a temperature of 24 to 28°C (75-82°C), perhaps a bit cooler during the winter dry season, and do not need extra lighting or more than a small undertank heat pad to be comfortable.

All specimens currently available are wild-collected, and they may not feed well in captivity, perhaps because of parasites. Those that eat will take mice and chicks of appropriate size, mostly living. Some specimens may refuse mice and feed only on chicks. It should be expected that juveniles will feed on frogs and lizards as well.

So far there has been little success breeding this species in captivity. Males are best distinguished from the typically larger females by probing, the hemipenis pouch being 12 to 14 subcaudal scales long. The clutch size seems to be small, possibly averaging only four eggs. They seem to be laid in the spring of the year (March and April), the young emerging about May. However, females also have laid in June, so it must be said that very little is known of the reproduction of the species. Gravid imported females have laid in captivity and the eggs have hatched when incubated at 30 to 31°C (86-88°F). Most eggs laid in captivity fail to hatch or produce dead, deformed young.

Recently specimens from Nicaragua and other Central American points have entered the hobby in small numbers, and the species is available again after a long period of rarity. Mexico no longer permits legal exports, and there is always a good chance that other countries will suddenly close down shipments. The species generally is available as small specimens at moderately high prices. This might be a good species for beginners if it were captive-bred. It is small, tolerant, and usually takes mice. What more might you ask?

Taxonomic History

Loxocemus bicolor was described by Cope in 1862 (*Proc. Acad. Nat. Sci. Phila.*, 13: 77). I've already discussed the status and history of *Loxocemus bicolor* and *L. sumichrasti*, so there is only one other name to consider. This is the snake described by Jan in 1862 (later than Cope's paper describing *L. bicolor*) as *Plastoseryx bronni* from "Americque meridionale?," basically meaning locality unknown (*Arch. fur Naturgesch.* and illustrated in the luxurious *Iconographie Generale des Ophidiens* in the same year). The snake appears to be a typical light-bellied form of the Neotropical Python, but with a small subocular scale keeping the supralabials from entering the eye. Because scales commonly fragment in pythons, this is considered insignificant. The type has 242 ventrals, indicating it probably came from Mexico and may be a senior synonym of *L. sumichrasti*. No one has ever questioned the generic status of this python, only its family relationships.

As a pythonine snake in the New World, *L. bicolor* is unique. Its relationships to the other pythons are debatable. Photo by R. D. Bartlett.

THE SUNBEAM SNAKES, FAMILY XENOPELTIDAE

Sunbeam snakes, represented by only the genus *Xenopeltis* with two described species, are one of the several groups of small burrowing snakes that are here treated as pythons. At first glance they bear little resemblance to your typical pythons, and they have been moved all around the board in trying to determine their relationships. They are beautiful but obscure snakes that seldom exceed a meter in length, have a rather narrow head, have only 15 rows of scales around the back, and are instantly recognizable by the extremely iridescent glow of their largely brown color pattern.

The problem in placing the sunbeams is that they show a mixture of supposedly primitive and specialized characters. The skull is extremely solid for a snake, probably partially an adaptation to semi-burrowing habits, the jaws are only weakly movable (the lower jaw, for instance, cannot be greatly distended to work large prey down the gullet), and the front portion of the lower jaw is slender and only loosely attached to the back portion, making it quite flexible though weak. There is no postfrontal bone as is found in most typical pythons, the ventral scales are quite wide, and the number of scale rows over the back is small, more like the colubrid snakes. The tail is short, typically only 10 to 12% of the total length.

Some specialists feel that sunbeam snakes are related to the cylinder snakes (Aniliidae), with which they share many features of skull shape and also a general appearance. Others feel they are intimately related to the Neotropical pythons (Loxocemidae), though to me the similarities are mostly adaptations for burrowing and retention of primitive characters. Because it is impossible to determine the actual relationships of the sunbeam snakes, they have no close relatives living today and are seemingly unknown in the dubious fossil record, and they have many unique combinations of characters, I go along with the group of herpetologists who recognize them as a full family of uncertain relationships.

Genus *Xenopeltis* Reinwardt, in Boie, 1827 (Oken's *Isis*: 564). Type species by orig. desig. *alvearius* Oppel = *unicolor*.

Cylindrical, stiff-bodied snakes with 15 scale rows (15-15-15), wide ventral scales, a short tail with subcaudals in two rows, and a distinct mental groove under the chin. The head is rather flattened and not distinct from the neck, the snout is rounded, and the eyes are small with the pupils vertically elliptical. The head shields are large and constant in development, including a pair of small internasals, large prefrontals, a triangular frontal, and a large median interparietal contacting the frontal and dividing a pair of large parietals. The loreal is absent or represented by the large preocular. Two supralabials enter the eye.

Two species currently are recognized:

KEY TO THE SPECIES OF XENOPELTIS

A. Ventrals under 160; subcaudals under 20; 7 supralabials; 1 postocular; southeastern China .... *X. hainanensis*

AA. Ventrals over 160; subcaudals over 21; 8 supralabials; 2 postoculars; Burma over Southeast Asia to Borneo and Sulawesi .... *X. unicolor*

XENOPELTIS HAINANENSIS
Hainan Sunbeam Snake

It came as a great surprise to Western herpetologists when this Chinese species was described in 1972. The Common Sunbeam Snake was thought to barely enter southern China and to then extend over most of southern Asia while showing almost no significant variation in scale and tooth counts. This Chinese species shows a large number of differences in both types of counts and, though it continues to be

virtually unknown in the West, must be recognized as a full species.

Description

In general appearance the Hainan Sunbeam Snake seems to be similar to the Common Sunbeam. It differs greatly in several counts, however, including:

Ventrals 152 to 157 (vs. 164 to 196 in *X. unicolor*)

Subcaudals 16 to 18 pairs (vs. 22 to 31)

Maxillary teeth 22 to 24 (vs. 35 to 45)

Supralabials 7 (vs. 8)

Postoculars 1 (vs. 2).

The tail is said to be even shorter than in the Common Sunbeam (7.1 to 7.7% of the total length), the anal plate is paired, the dorsal scales are smooth and in 15-15-15 rows, and

Head and midbody views of *X. hainanensis*.

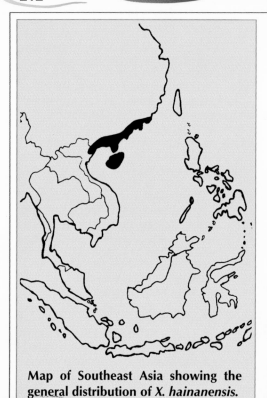

Map of Southeast Asia showing the general distribution of *X. hainanensis.*

apply to most Common Sunbeams, and even a few Common Sunbeams have dark bellies.

Natural History

Originally described from the large island of Hainan off the southeastern coast of China, the species now is recorded also from Guangxi Province eastward to Zhejiang Province, basically the entire southeastern Chinese coast. This is a low-elevation coastal region. One of the type specimens was found in grasses under a basket of young pineapple plants near a harbor. It can be assumed that the snake prefers low, moist habitats under logs and debris.

I've seen nothing on the natural history and husbandry of the Hainan Sunbeam Snake, but it is not impossible that it currently is being imported for the herp hobby but is not recognized as a species distinct from the Common Sunbeam. Hobbyists definitely should keep an eye out for this species, as many other herps are entering the market from the same region of China today. The easiest recognition characters (assuming there are no real distinctions in color pattern) might be the number of supralabial scales, seven (only two following the labials that enter the eye) in this species and eight (three following the labials that enter the eye) in the Common Sunbeam, and the number of postoculars (only one in the Hainan Sunbeam, apparently always two in the Common).

supralabials 4 and 5 enter the eye (preceded by 3 supralabials and followed by 2). The type specimens were 628mm (a male) and 521mm (a female) long. All these counts come from the original description and are based on only the two types, so it should be expected that the counts will prove more variable.

The Hainan Sunbeam was described as being indigo brown above with a strong iridescence and pale bluish gray or light brown below (shiny white in the Common Sunbeam). The lowest row of dorsal scales was similar in color to the belly, and there were two rows of small white spots on the lower dorsal scale rows. The underside of the tail was indigo brown. Except for the darker belly, this description could easily

Taxonomic History

Xenopeltis hainanensis was originally described in 1972 by Hu and Djao in *Acta Zoologica Sinica*, 24(4): 379-384. Djao now spells his name Zhao due to one of the several changes in westernization of Chinese spellings and is the foremost Chinese herpetologist. The original description is available to Western herpetologists as *Smithsonian Herp. Info. Serv. Publication No. 53*, an English translation of the major parts of the paper. There are no indications that the ranges of the two species of sunbeams overlap, though it is not impossible, but until (or if ever) a broad area of intergradation is discovered they should be retained as full species.

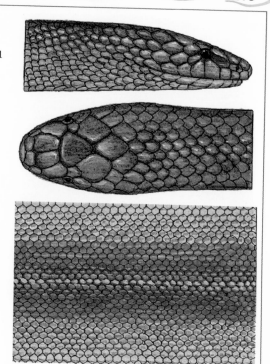

Head and midbody views of *X. unicolor.*

XENOPELTIS UNICOLOR
Common Sunbeam Snake

Once you've seen a Common Sunbeam Snake in the flesh, you are unlikely to ever misidentify it. It has a distinctive iridescent quality even if in poor condition, and the body, though extremely strong, feels stiff and relatively inflexible. The large scales in only a few rows (just 15 over the entire body) also help distinguish it from other python-like snakes, while the arrangement of the head scales is unique if you take a couple of seconds to look at them closely.

Description

These are cylindrical, rather heavy-bodied snakes that seldom exceed a meter in length and have a somewhat flattened head that is not distinct from the body (there is no obvious neck). The snout is not especially enlarged and is rather rounded, with an obvious rostral scale. The ventral scales are wide, the tail is fairly short (9 to 14% of the total length), and the subcaudal scales are paired; the anal plate is split. The scales are highly polished (covered with very fine ridges under magnification) and iridescent. They are large and in only 15 rows over the back one head length behind the head, at midbody, and one head length before the vent (15-15-15).

From above, the rostral scale is broadly visible and followed by a pair of small internasals. The frontal is a rather long triangle and is preceded by a pair of large prefrontals. The supraocular scale is small and oddly angled, wedged

X. unicolor has a stiff feel when handled and rather large body scales. There should be little trouble identifying this snake. Photo by R. D. Bartlett.

between a large parietal scale behind and an elongated preocular in front. The frontal is followed by a large interparietal that is similar in size to the frontal and to the almost equally large parietals. Commonly there are three greatly enlarged scales behind the parietals and interparietal before the small body scales are reached. From the side, the nostril is placed between a pair of nasal scales, and the large strap-like preocular fills the space between the eye and the posterior nasal. (The preocular may represent a fused loreal plus preocular.) There are two large postoculars that are only a bit smaller than the temporal scales. There are eight supralabials, the first extending upward to contact the edge of the internasal. The fourth and fifth supralabials are vertically elongated and help form

the lower margin of the orbit (i.e., they enter the eye). The posterior three supralabials are low and rather elongated. There are eight infralabials, three in contact with the single pair of chin shields. The mental groove is deep and obvious. The eye is small, dark, and has a vertical pupil.

There are 164 to 196 ventral scales and 22 to 31 pairs of subcaudals. The lowermost (first) row of dorsal scales is obviously enlarged compared to the other scales of the back.

The hemipenis is weakly but distinctly bilobed and has a bifurcate sulcus, each branch ending in a distinct disk without ornamentation. There are a few flounces near the middle of the organ, which appears very simple. The left lung is about half the length of the right lung. There are no pelvic remnants, neither external spurs or internal pelvic and femur bones. The chromosomes are similar to those of most other pythons and boas, 2N=36, with 16 macrochromosomes and 20 microchromosomes.

The color pattern of adult Common Sunbeams is not complicated. Basically it is a deep purplish brown above, creamy white below, with the lowermost dorsal scale row pale yellowish. There is no distinct dark pattern above, but because the posterior edge of each scale is paler than the body of the scale, there often is the appearance of indistinct dark and pale spots in lines along the back. The color is darkest at midback and becomes paler on the sides. The chin and lower lip are pale like the belly, though there may be large brown blotches on the chin most prominent in juveniles. The underside of the tail often is heavily blotched with purplish brown. The upper lip may be pale (white to yellow) or dark brown. Melanistic specimens, uniformly dark purplish brown above and below, are not uncommon, and albinistic specimens also have been reported.

Hatchling to half-grown Sunbeams are much like the adults, but they have a broad pale collar across the back of the head and the neck. The width and color of the collar vary considerably, but generally it is yellow to creamy white and at least the snout area of the head is dark brown. There may be brown blotches at the anterior edge of

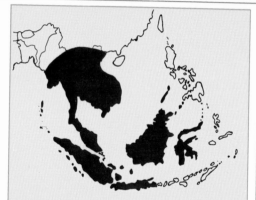

Map of Southeast Asia showing the general natural range of *X. unicolor.*

the collar. The collar gradually becomes less distinct with growth but may be visible in some large adults as a pale area on the nape.

The skull is distinctive among living snakes in being very solid, with little mobility of the individual bones. The premaxilla is large, toothed, and in broad contact with the maxillaries. The postfrontal is absent. The supratemporal is short and heavy, as is the quadrate, allowing little extension of the lower jaws. However, the lower jaw is distinctively slender and has most of the dentary bone free from the mandibular and extending well posterior over the mandibular bone, allowing quite a bit of limited mobility in that area. The coronoid bone is very small and displaced posteriorly (it once was thought to be absent). There are 8 to 10 premaxillary teeth and 35 to 45 maxillary teeth. On average, there are 13 palatine teeth, 11 pterygoid teeth, and 35 dentary (mandibular) teeth.

Adults typically are 70 cm to a meter long, with the record appearing to be 1328mm.

Hatchlings probably are about 250 to 275mm long. Adults may weight 650 to over 700 grams.

Natural Variation

Although no subspecies are recognized and there appear to be no range-related variations in scale counts, there are indications that two lip colors occur in this snake. In the light-lipped form the upper lip is pale, usually white or very pale yellow. This is the common form that apparently is found over all of continental Southeast Asia and also on Java. However, specimens from Sumatra, Banka, Borneo, and the southern Philippines have the upper lip strongly blotched with dark brown. This distinction was first noted by Mertens in 1943 and to the best of my knowledge has never been researched further. Both lip colors may occur on Java, further complicating the situation. Additionally, it is possible that some specimens from the southern Philippines may retain a distinct pale collar into adulthood.

Natural History

The Common Sunbeam Snake has a large range extending from Burma (and the Andaman Islands of India) and perhaps adjacent China (no trustworthy records) eastward to Vietnam and south over the Malay Peninsula into Indonesia (Sumatra, Java, Banka) plus Borneo and Sulawesi (the Celebes) and Palawan in the southern Philippines. It tends to be more commonly found on the mainland than on the islands. Old records from southeastern China now are referred to X. hainanensis.

This typically is a species of low elevations, often along the coast, and it tends to be associated with loose soils and relatively open forests. It not uncommonly is found near canals, fields, and inhabited areas, and may be taken crossing roads at night. It is mostly nocturnal, but also may hunt during the morning and evening on cloudy and rainy days. It is not a strong burrower, but it often is found a few centimeters below the surface under logs and debris and also may inhabit mammal burrows.

In nature the Common Sunbeam Snake seems to feed mostly on snakes, lizards, and especially frogs. It takes rather small prey because the teeth are small and the jaws not very mobile. Often it just grabs a food animal and swallows it, but with larger or more active prey it may throw one or two loose coils over the body and constrict the prey. The snakes can be slow feeders, taking over 30 minutes to overpower and swallow a small frog. They also eat small mammals (mice, shrews) and nestling birds that they probably find dead on the ground. There are no indications that they climb to raid bird nests.

These sunbeam snakes appear to be solitary. They are very calm and gentle, seldom or never (?) biting. They are very strong, however, and when you pick one up you know it is on your hand. When excited they may rapidly vibrate the short tail, but this display is rare in captivity.

I've yet to see an account of reproduction in this species, but it is thought to lay eggs. Females with from 6 to 17 eggs in their bodies have been recorded, and this probably represents the actual clutch size. The sexes are not distinguishable externally, though the base of the male's tail may be somewhat swollen to accommodate the hemipenes.

human population growth in the area. Once a commonly exported snake for the pet industry, today it is at least partially protected over its range and is not as available. It is too small to use for the skin trade, so at least it is not threatened in that regard.

Husbandry

This is one of the most simple snakes to care for. It can be kept in a 20-gallon-long terrarium with

X. unicolor is an undemanding captive. For the most part, it only needs warmth, food, water, and a soft substrate for burrowing. Photo by R. D. Bartlett.

Females are mature at a length of at least 653mm. The young hatch at the beginning of or during the rainy season (when most food is available) and appear to be over 230mm long when they leave the nest.

Though locally common in Thailand and much of Southeast Asia, the Common Sunbeam Snake may be dropping in numbers because of the vast

a substrate of soil, peat moss, and sand to allow it to burrow and hide during the day. A substrate about 100 to 150mm deep makes the animal feel at home. However, some keepers have successfully maintained the species on newspaper with sufficient hide boxes to make the snake comfortable. Remember, this is not a very strong burrower. It does well at temperatures between 24 and 32°C (75-90°F), with a 5 degree drop at night. They do not bask (though a warm area on the cage floor might be suggested) and don't need special lighting.

Frogs and mice are the easiest foods to supply in the terrarium. Young specimens may refuse mice and have to be gradually shifted from a frog and lizard diet to mice over a period of several months. You may have to rub the mice with frog skin to induce the snake to feed. Some adults take mice and chicks right from the start, which certainly is easier than trying to provide frogs during the winter. Keep the prey small—remember the small gape of this species. Provide three or four frogs or lizards (or mice) of appropriate size at each meal. Feed about every 10 to 14 days. Captives molt often. Water can be provided in a bowl (which might not be used by some individuals) or by spraying the substrate at regular intervals.

Common Sunbeams will eat other snakes in captivity, including specimens over a meter long. They cannot be safely kept in colonies.

It is possible that this species lays during the dry season in nature and a cycle of moist and dry surroundings may have to be initiated to induce reproduction in captivity. I am not aware of any successful breeding of this species in captivity, but probably few hobbyists have ever tried to maintain more than one or two specimens (unsexed) at a time.

This species has been known to live well over 12 years in captivity and probably is long-lived in nature as well.

Taxonomic History

The Common Sunbeam Snake first was described from a Reinwardt (also commonly spelled Reinhardt) manuscript published in 1827 by Boie in an obscure and controversial journal known as Oken's *Isis*. The generally accepted citation is *Xenopeltis unicolor* Reinwardt in Boie, 1827, *Isis*: 564. Boie was a German naturalist working on a herpetology of Java, based largely on the collections of many Dutch naturalists in Java. He accepted a position in the Dutch Natural History Commission of the Dutch Indies in 1825 and died in Java in 1827. (The Java area was a true "whitemen's grave" at that time.) His numerous unpublished manuscripts, along with those by other deceased Dutch naturalists, were to provide material for many papers by later herpetologists.

When Reinwardt described *X. unicolor* from Java, he also described two other species that now are considered to be synonyms: *X. concolor* and (based on the juvenile with a white collar) *X. leucocephala*. All are from Java. Schlegel's 1837 name *Xenopeltis xenopeltis* is a replacement name that was not necessary under the modern rules. Other than moving the genus and species around from family to family, there has been little taxonomic attention given to this snake over the last 150 years.

Madagascar. The little island is less than 2 km in diameter and has a total area of 151 hectares (374 acres), much of it probably originally covered with scrubby palms and other woody plants. Several centuries ago seamen introduced goats and rabbits to the island (and also to the smaller islands nearby) and they destroyed virtually all the plants on the island, turning it into a near-desert. As the habitat disappeared, the eight reptile species on the island (six lizards and two split-jaws) dwindled in number as food insects (and lizard prey) also dwindled. The plight of the rare split-jaws was realized about half a century ago, but the snakes have always been rare in collections and poorly studied. Several British-sponsored expeditions to Round Island in the 1970's and 1980's led to the collection of a few specimens of the Slender Split-jaw for the collection of the Jersey Wildlife Trust in the Channel Islands, where they now have been maintained and bred over several generations.

By the mid-1970's the population of Slender Split-jaws may have dropped to under 75 individuals, but a massive campaign to remove goats and rabbits from the island has led to restoration of much of the original flora and an increase in both insects and lizards. Currently the Slender Split-jaw is thought to number several hundred individuals on Round Island, probably as many as the island can support. The snake is now known to be a lizard-eater, adults perhaps specializing in the large skinks that live on the island, while juveniles feed on geckos. The divided maxillary bones aid the snake in gripping the curved body of a heavily plated skink. The snake is terrestrial, not arboreal as formerly thought, and seldom is found even a meter above the surface. It lives in shallow burrows and under leaves and other debris. It is reported that it often lies with the head buried under debris and the tail exposed and wiggling as a lure to attract lizards.

Based on limited observations on Round Island and a good bit of information from captivity, the Slender Split-jaw probably lays its eggs between March and July. Clutches vary from 3 or 4 to 11 eggs. Other details are given in the Husbandry section.

The Slender Split-jaw is strictly protected, and even visits to Round Island are not permitted without special paperwork. The object of the Jersey Wildlife Trust breeding program is to produce specimens for possible reintroduction to Round Island or nearby islands if the natural habitats are ever completely regenerated. This may actually be possible, but it also is possible that eventually these snakes might reach the private market in small numbers.

Husbandry

These are tough snakes to maintain and also hard to breed. It took the Jersey Wildlife Trust several years to adjust their animals to captive conditions, and they had many losses. It also took over five years before the colony began to breed on a regular basis. The snakes are maintained in glass terraria with standard substrates. The Jersey animals have been shifted from a lizard diet to mice, which required scenting the mice with lizards. They are kept at high temperatures of 30°C (86°F) during the summer, 26°C (79°F) during the winter, the temperature allowed to drop at night. The colony is provided with a strict light cycle, 13.5 hours during the summer, dropping to 11.5 hours during the winter.

Clutches at first were mostly infertile, but eventually a fair hatching percentage was attained. Incubation of the clutches was from 62 to 72 days. The young are about 180mm long, very thin, and delicate. Most have to be force-fed on small pieces of chicken, lizard, and heart meat if they do not feed naturally by two weeks of age. The young desiccate easily, so they are maintained in individual gallon containers on tissue paper and given a water bowl. Force-feeding is complicated and there are many losses.

Taxonomic History

The species was described by Schlegel in 1837 (*Phys. Serp.*, 2: 396) as a *Boa*, but Gray in 1842 established the new genus *Casarea* for it. It also served as the type species of *Leptoboa* Dumeril & Bibron, 1844. The uniqueness of the species has never been in doubt, though the species always has been considered very rare. It is here transferred to *Bolyeria* because there are few substantial differences from *B. multocarinata*. Even the color patterns of the two are similar, and the head scalation with two large prefrontals extending down to the supralabials is distinctive, as are the keeled scales.

BOLYERIA MULTOCARINATA
Burrowing Split-jaw

Because the head of this split-jaw is somewhat rounded and not set off from the body by a distinct neck, at first it gives the appearance of one of the burrowing sand boas, *Eryx*. This species may be extinct, and there are few specimens in collections, most observations in the literature being based on examination of only a handful of specimens.

Description

Cylindrical, heavy-bodied snakes with small, rounded, and somewhat flattened heads not distinct from the body (no neck). The snout is rounded but the rostral is not especially enlarged. The ventral scales are wide, the tail moderately long (about 20% of total length) and bluntly pointed. The subcaudal scales are single, as is the anal plate. The body scales are small, rather hexagonal in shape, and bear 3 to 5 short keels. There are 53 to 57 rows of scales at midbody. The lowest row of scales is smooth and consists of alternating larger and smaller scales.

From above the rostral scale is wide and barely visible. The small internasals are vaguely squarish and may be partially fused. There is a pair of large prefrontals that may show signs of partially splitting; the prefrontals extend downward to contact the supralabials. The supraocular on each side is large and may have irregular margins. Where the frontal should be there commonly is an irregular pair of shields that may have especially broken posterior margins. Somewhat enlarged scales behind the eyes may represent the parietals. From the side, the nostril (which is somewhat dorsal in position) pierces a single large nasal scale. The prefrontal occupies the space between the nasal and the preoculars and is in contact with one or two supralabials. There are two preoculars (sometimes broken) and four or five postoculars. There are nine supralabials, the fourth entering the orbit; the anterior supralabials are large and squarish, the second especially large. The 12 or so infralabials are small, only the first and second in contact with the small chin shields. There is no mental groove, small scales extending forward to the chin shields. The eye is small and silvery with a vertically elliptical pupil.

There are 192 to 200 ventral scales and 83 to 92 single subcaudals.

The hemipenis has been described as deeply split, bifurcate for over 80% of its length, the shaft about 19% of the

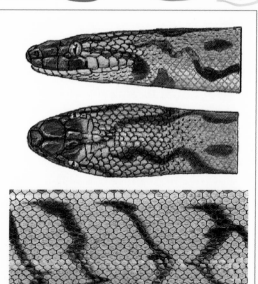

Head and midbody views of *B. multocarinata.*

length of the organ; the sulcus divides at about 67% of the shaft length. The left lung is about 14% of the length of the right. There is no trace of pelvic remnants (no spurs).

Adults (hatchlings appear to be unrecorded) are pale tan to grayish brown above, yellowish below. There are irregular darker brown bars and spots low on the sides that may partially fuse in an irregular manner to produce an open network of dark lines over the back. There are dark vertical bars on the sides of the tail, and the belly is heavily spotted and blotched with dark brown. Individuals seem to vary from almost uniformly brown to heavily marked with a broken dark pattern. There is a dark stripe back from the eye to above the angle of the jaws, and the snout has been depicted as dark brown.

The skull is much like that of the Slender Split-jaw but is a bit heavier, wider, and more consolidated in keeping with the apparent burrowing habits of the species. The jaws also are a bit heavier than in the Slender Split-jaw, but the same pattern of enlarged teeth on the anterior maxillary segment and smaller ones behind applies, as does the enlarged teeth behind the symphysis of the mandibles. The coronoid bone is small but present and the postfrontal is absent. There are no premaxillary teeth. On average, there are 18 maxillary teeth, 8 palatine teeth, 11 pterygoid teeth, and 15 dentary (mandibular) teeth.

Adults, as far as known, average about 75 cm in length, with the apparent record at 1080mm.

Natural Variation

This is one of the most poorly known of all the snakes and it has never been really studied. The color pattern varies considerably, perhaps with age.

Natural History

This species of Round Island endemic (no fossils are yet known from other islands) is assumed to be a burrower, but actually almost nothing is known of its natural history. The shape certainly agrees with burrowing habits. Because it has a jaw structure similar to *B. dussumieri*, it is assumed to feed on skinks and geckos. The last probable record of this species was in 1975, it always was rare before that, and it is assumed (perhaps incorrectly) to be extinct. However, burrowers are notoriously difficult to sample and it is possible that a few specimens still survive. If this is true, then as the natural flora of Round Island returns the snakes also may reappear.

No data are available on reproduction in this species, and it apparently never has been maintained in hobby terraria. Because *B. dussumieri* lays eggs, it can be assumed that this species also is an egg-layer, but there is no evidence to back up this supposition.

The Burrowing Split-jaw is completely protected, if it still survives.

Taxonomic History

Boie, in *Isis* (1827: 513) described this snake as an *Eryx*, calling it *multocarinata*, probably as a misprint for *multicarinata*. However, Boie never corrected the spelling (he died in 1827) and we are stuck with the *o* rather than *i* spelling. Ten years later Schlegel (*Phys. Serp.*, 2: 19) described a specimen as *Tortrix pseudo-eryx*, which Gray in 1842 made the type species of his new genus *Bolyeria*. Boie's name *mult(i)carinata* became the type species of Dumeril & Bibron's new genus *Platygaster* in 1844. By the time of Boulenger's catalogue in 1893, the name of this snake was much as it is today but with variant spellings of both generic and specific names: *Bolieria multicarinata*.

CARING FOR PYTHONS

Most of the pythons are large snakes that are inactive during the day, resting in a favored corner of the cage under the cover of a hide box or a log. Some spend much of their time resting in branches, while some like to soak. In the earlier chapters I've discussed most of the essentials for successfully maintaining each species of python, so this chapter serves simply as a summary of basic techniques used for keeping your "average" pythons.

PRECAUTIONS

If you keep pythons, you probably will be bitten. Many pythons are quick to react to movements of all types and assume that anything that comes at them is either predator or prey. In the case of small pythons the bite is no more serious than that of a kingsnake or rat snake; you will bleed a bit and have some pain for a few minutes, and then forget about it. Just clean the wound carefully with hydrogen peroxide and a general cleanser such as povidone iodine and bandage it if necessary. Watch out for infections (python bites are notoriously dirty) and see a doctor if any complications result.

Large pythons are another matter entirely. Any python over 2 or 3 meters in length can be perceived as seriously dangerous. The front teeth of larger pythons are long and very sharp and can penetrate deeply. A bite often is accompanied by some crushing and bruising as well as the usual puncture wounds and bleeding. Deep puncture wounds easily may become infected, sometimes dangerously so, and the bruising may actually crush cartilages in the finger joints. Some pythons instinctively go for the face, and the bite of even a 2-meter python to the nose or cheek may require medical attention.

If you are bitten by a large python, it might be best to have a doctor check the wound and give you a course of antibiotics. The doctor should check for the presence of amoebas in the wound, as some pythons carry infectious protozoans on the

Large pythons require very careful handling. This is an amelanistic Burmese Python. Photo by I. Francais.

When taking a python out of a hide box, move slowly and carefully to avoid startling it. The bottom python is a Diamond Python, *P. s. spilotus*, and the one in hand is a Diamond-Carpet intergrade. Photo by I. Francais.

What this means to a keeper is that a large python is attracted to warmer surfaces of the body, such as the neck and arms, and will attempt to coil there, especially if it has struck you and gotten you confused with food. The neck especially is warmer because of the large blood vessels just under the skin. If you let a large python coil around your neck, you are asking for trouble and may very well get it. Pythons also have a tendency to become tangled in long hair, something to remember when taking a python for a walk.

Yes, large pythons, especially Reticulated Pythons, Asian Rock Pythons, African Rock Pythons, and Scrub Pythons, have the ability to kill a human. Yes, every year or two a keeper does something really stupid and pays for it with his or her life. Serious and fatal accidents usually result from a combination of alcohol or drugs and carelessness. One of the classic fatal accidents involved a keeper who held a dead rabbit under his chin while feeding his large python.

If your python is over 3 meters in length, it never should be handled by only one person. It will take two people to uncoil it if there is an accident during feeding or cage maintenance. It may take two people to get it in

gums. Additionally, there may be broken teeth imbedded in the wound that may slow healing. Your tetanus immunization should be up to date as well.

Most pythons are ambush predators, lying in wait along a game trail and quickly striking at suitable prey as it passes within reach. The snake then throws one or several coils over the prey and constricts it until it stops breathing because the ribs and diaphragm (if a bird or mammal) cannot move. Almost all pythons have heat sensing pits in the scales of the upper jaw and the rostral scale that let them distinguish small differences in temperatures, the difference between the body temperature of the prey and the air temperature. Even pythons that lack obvious pits still may be able to sense temperature differences. They respond to struggling by the prey by increasing the pressure of the coils.

and out of its cage. If you are bitten, it may take a second person to drive you to the hospital. Always have a support person available to help you in case of trouble.

Large pythons may be a danger to pets and small children, so their cages must be sturdily build and securely latched or preferably locked. Never let a large python have the run of the house. Babies really have been killed by loose pet pythons.

Always follow the local laws and permit requirements that your state, province, city, or town may apply to the keeping of large snakes. No matter how much you feel that your 4-meter Burmese is a perfectly tame and predictable pet, it is a dangerous animal to everyone else. You cannot hide a large python, and you probably cannot afford the fines if your neighbor turns you in. Some cities may simply prohibit all snakes over a certain size (2 or 3 meters is not uncommon). In such a situation, you may have to move if you wish to legally keep large pythons.

CAGING

Python cages can be relatively simple as long as they are sturdily constructed and can be securely covered. Though glass aquaria work well for small animals, larger pythons will require specially built cages of wood, plastic, and Plexiglas. Fortunately, the inactive lifestyles of most pythons mean that you don't need a cage much longer than the length of the python for it to be comfortable. Pythons don't need exercise.

Note the size of the snake vs. the size of the keeper. You must exercise extreme caution when dealing with any of the giant pythons, such as this Reticulated Python. They can cause serious and fatal injuries. Photo by L. Rossiter.

As a general rule, a terrarium for a small to medium python should be 1 to 2 meters in length, about half that in width, and at least a meter high. The lid should be partially screened to allow air flow and also to allow the rays of a heating bulb to penetrate easily. Different keepers prefer different substrates, but aspen bedding, small smooth pebbles, washed sand, and newspaper all have been recommended for one circumstance or another. Obviously a python that prefers it dry should not be kept in a cage with a moisture-retaining substrate, while one that is thin-skinned and needs lots of moisture (water pythons and White-lips, for instance) may like to have at least part of the cage bottom covered with sphagnum so there is always a moist area to retire to.

A hide box always should be available. Snakes like to relax with their bodies touching a solid object, and they like cramped hide boxes. An overly large hide box may make your python uncomfortable. Many different styles of hide boxes can be purchased at your pet shop, and large curved slabs of cork bark or split logs also serve well. Moisture-loving species may like having the hide box partially filled with sphagnum that is kept a bit moist; this also may help them have smooth molts without any problems of adhering pieces.

Almost all pythons like a large water bowl in their terrarium, and many will drink from it, defecate in it, and bathe in it. Obviously the water must be kept clean at all times to prevent reinfection from intestinal parasites passed in the feces.

A python's waterbowl must be changed frequently, since most pythons are prone to soak and defecate in their bowls. This is a Diamond-Carpet Python intergrade.   Photo by I. Francais.

Species that are partially or mostly arboreal (climbers) will need several large and sturdily anchored branches on which to relax. Some species, such as the Green Tree Python, will spend the entire day on a branch, coming down at night to feed. Be sure that branches are not placed directly under each other if more than one python is in the cage, as they shortly will become covered with feces and will have to be removed and cleaned.

Because they are durable and easy to clean, many keepers use molded plastic cages for their pythons. This is Ramsay's Python, *Aspidites ramsayi*. Photo by I. Francais.

Small pythons, such as the White-eyed, do very well in small quarters such as the racks of plastic boxes used for large breeding colonies of kingsnakes. Others, such as Green Tree Pythons, need large terraria that are distinctly vertical for them to feel at home.

HEAT AND LIGHT

Most pythons do not need artificial light to prosper. They are nocturnal and normally not active during the day anyway. They do respond to sunlight in the way of day length, however, and if at all possible their terrarium should be exposed indirectly (as through unshaded windows) to normal day lengths during most of the year. Many pythons appear to breed better if given about 14 hours of light per day for eight or nine months, reducing the light gradually to ten hours during two months of winter. If you use artificial lights, they should be positioned outside the

Even small and hatchling pythons are powerful constrictors. This Faded Python, *Antaresia childreni,* is killing a fuzzy mouse. Photo by K. H. Switak.

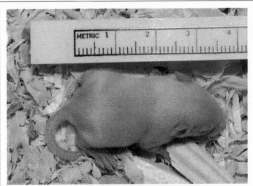

Fuzzy mice are the usual first food for most pythons. Photo by M. Walls

terrarium to prevent burns; full-spectrum fluorescents, though recently considered of questionable value by some hobbyists, will do no harm and may improve the snake's outlook on life in some indefinable way.

Almost all pythons like to have a basking light over one corner of the terrarium. Gravid females of many species bask for hours each day, as may juveniles. A warm corner also helps promote a thermal gradient from warmest to coolest temperatures in the terrarium. The basking light should be placed over a favorite branch or rock, not over the water bowl or hide box.

Almost all pythons do well at air

The hatchlings of small pythons, like *Antaresia*, normally eat pinky mice. Photo by M. Walls.

temperatures between 26 and 30°C (79 and 86°F) with a corner a few degrees warmer. Under-tank heaters work well in maintaining such temperatures most of the year, especially when a basking light is on for several hours a day. Almost all pythons also seem to do better if the temperature is allowed to drop a few degrees at night; constant temperatures are not necessary and not desirable. Additionally, most pythons like it a bit cooler for a couple of months during the winter (usually this represents a change from dry season to wet season in the tropics).

Common finches can be used to tempt reluctant feeders. Photo by M. Gilroy.

FEEDING

In captivity, the most popular pythons feed on rodents, rabbits, and birds (chicks and chickens, especially) of appropriate size. Hatchlings are started on mice and then move on to rats, hamsters, gerbils, guinea pigs, and rabbits. Zoos feed very large pythons piglets and even goats, but such are not realistic foods for most hobbyist situations. The cost of feeding a large or even a medium python may be quite high, a factor to remember when making your initial purchase of that cute baby.

Chicks are a common food item for pythons, especially those known to heavily feed on birds in the wild. Photo by M. Walls.

Wild-caught imported pythons may be too heavily stressed to feed on their own and may have to be force-fed at first. Forced-feeding is an art that should be learned from a practiced hand because it is stressful to the snake and may be dangerous to the handler(s) as well. Hatchlings that do not feed on their own for several weeks after hatching also may have to be force-fed, an even more delicate operation.

Hatchlings of many pythons apparently feed on lizards in the wild, usually preferring skinks and geckos. They may require such foods in captivity as well. Because lizards often are not easily obtained, most breeders try to make their hatchlings switch to mice if at all possible. They may require scenting a mouse by rubbing it with a lizard, especially the blood from a broken lizard tail or the open body cavity. Some breeders put a lizard in a blender with a bit of water to form a "lizard concoction" and then rub this over the mouse. Hatchlings of some pythons are notoriously

While it is safer to feed pre-killed prey, many pythons, especially wild-caught specimens, will insist on live food. This Calabar Python, *Calabaria reinhardti,* is eating a pinky rat. Photo by K. H. Switak.

Green Tree Pythons, *P. viridis,* normally feed best right from their perch. This is their normal posture when swallowing prey. Photo by K. H. Switak.

How much you feed and how often obviously will depend on the species, the season, and the size of the python. As a general rule, young pythons feed more often than older ones and very large pythons feed at long intervals. Never try to get your python to swallow food items that cause it a great deal of effort and excessive jaw distension. Like most animals, pythons prefer smaller prey that is easily overcome and swallowed. Excessively large prey items may cause jaw and esophagus damage and stress the snake.

Of course I don't have to remind you that living rodents should never be left overnight with a snake of any size.

GENERAL HEALTH

I've long held that the recognition and treatment of even the most basic ills of reptiles are beyond the capabilities of the average hobbyist. By this I do not mean to imply that hobbyists are stupid or uneducated, just that diagnosis and treatment of almost all illnesses require very specialized education and experience as well as generally unavailable equipment. In England it is illegal for a non-veterinarian to give veterinary advice or attempt to treat any but

difficult to feed, and many die. Fortunately, most pythons do not begin to feed until after their first shed, which commonly is one or two weeks after hatchling. Some hatchlings appear to go without food for six weeks or more after hatching, but they are exceptions. Most python babies should be feeding by the time they are four to six weeks old.

Rats are probably the most common food item for captive, adult pythons, Photo by S. Shore.

the most common conditions of pets, and perhaps this would be sound policy in the United States as well.

Pythons, with very few exceptions, are expensive animals to purchase and maintain, and it is to your best interest to make arrangements with a qualified reptile vet the moment you begin to seriously consider purchasing a python. Once rarities, reptile vets today can be found in or near most large cities, and many advertise in the reptile magazines and also in the yellow pages. Veterinary organizations recently have realized the growing importance of reptiles to the pet industry and some now offer their members special seminars and courses to improve their knowledge of reptile medicine. Your pet shop probably has an agreement with a local vet to handle their reptile problems, and they may be happy to refer you to their vet. Just be sure the veterinarian you use is interested in reptile medicine, is qualified to treat pythons, and is willing to handle the problems that go along with the giant snakes.

The best way to be sure you have a healthy snake is to purchase a captive-bred specimen that is guaranteed to be feeding on a food you can supply. Wild-caught imports have intestinal

Many pythons will eat birds in the wild, and it does no harm to offer them to pet pythons. This is an Angolan Python, *P. anchietae,* eagerly devouring a lovebird. Photo by K. H. Switak.

Part of the keeper's responsibility is to provide his/her snakes with proper medical care as necessary. This Ball Python, *P. regius*, is receiving an antibiotic injection. Photo by I. Francais.

pythons, such as Blood Pythons, always look obese, but most are more slender and have the proper muscle tone.

You can detect and treat mites and ticks in pythons. Ticks often are abundant on imported specimens. They may appear as the usual blood-inflated sacks between scales almost anywhere on the body or as small black spots wedged under the free edges of the ventrals. Ticks can be removed by using pointed tweezers (forceps, the term I prefer) to grasp them firmly as close to the skin as possible, twisting a bit, and then pulling. To prevent infection, put a dab of povidone iodine on each tick site. Small ticks may be difficult to remove by hand but usually can be killed by following the treatment for mites. Ticks almost never can reproduce in the terrarium, and once all are removed your problems should be finished. Because of the Lyme's disease scare, many people today are reluctant to handle ticks, but as long as you do not squeeze removed ticks between your fingers there is no danger at all with snake ticks as far as known.

Mites can be treated in many different ways, but the use of synthetic pyrethrums in the form

parasites that will have to be treated by your vet immediately (unless your dealer can provide you with proof the specimen already has been wormed) and will be stressed. They may be dehydrated, scarred, and have badly damaged snouts and broken tails. Any major purchase should be vetted immediately after you obtain it.

The eyes of pythons are always bright and glossy, never dull and sunken (unless before a shed). No python should have cheesy white material in the mouth or be blowing bubbles through the nostrils. Pythons do not breathe with their mouths open unless they are sick, and they never rasp when they breathe. Never purchase a python that may be ill—it will cause you no end of troubles and may infect any other specimens in your collection.

Beware obese pythons. These may not be able to reproduce and may have shortened lives. Some of sprays and rinses works well. Mites are tiny blackish red spider-like animals that often can be seen crawling in the corners of the cage at night or recognized by the silvery sheen of their feces on the snake's body. Mites lay eggs in the cage, usually in tiny crevices in bark or in the substrate, so any treatment has to be repeated at least twice at intervals to be sure the next generation is killed. Follow the instructions on the product label for most efficient use of any mite remedy.

Recently a simple manual removal method for mites has been suggested that might work in terraria containing small pythons. Mites tend to climb up the sides of a terrarium and accumulate near the upper frame at night. If a strip of folded double-sided sticky tape is applied along the upper frame of the terrarium, the mites will climb up to the folded crease in the tape and get stuck, soon dying. All stages of the mites will be caught in the tape, from young nymphs to gravid females. The tape is removed and disposed of weekly and new tape installed. This method may work in problem cases where it is not possible to completely clean out and sterilize all the cage furnishings after a treatment with a spray or rinse.

Never be afraid to ask your dealer for help if you have a problem. Never be afraid to visit a qualified vet (with an appointment) if your python appears to be out of sorts, even if you don't see anything really wrong with it. Vets won't work for free, but they may be the best friend your snake will ever have. Be prepared to pay a fair price for a worthwhile service.

Misting the cage will help your python shed its skin easily. Providing a rough stone or branch helps as well. This is a shedding Angolan Python, *P. anchietae*. Photo by P. Freed.

This is a pair of Green Tree Pythons, *P. viridis,* mating. Although they are still expensive, these pythons are now being bred in good numbers. Photo by K. H. Switak.

BREEDING PYTHONS

To many hobbyists the proof that they are successful is the breeding of their pythons. In fact, almost all hobby literature features this as the main or perhaps only thrust of keeping snakes in captivity. Personally, I feel that this is a passing aberration of hobby literature. Not every keeper can be a breeder, nor should they try. Breeding most pythons requires access to at least two or three specimens in excellent condition and of the proper age. They must be properly housed, and there must be sufficient room and equipment to maintain the hatchlings.

If you are very lucky and a careful breeder, you may be able to recoup your investment in the parents by selling young. However, at the moment there are literally dozens, perhaps hundreds, of small breeders of pythons in the United States, plus a few dozen large-scale commercial breeders. There also are many importers who can supply specimens at lower cost per head than any breeder. If you successfully breed a species that is common, you may never be able to sell the young. This is the problem at the moment with albino Burmese Pythons. In just a few years they went from exotic rarities to common wholesale items that are hard to sell; some pet shops sell young Burmese Pythons for not much more than Corn Snakes—and pythons are much more expensive to feed and maintain than Corn Snakes. The only real money in breeding is to be made either in mass production in commercial quantities of common species or being among the first to successfully breed and sell a rare species or variety before everyone else is doing it.

Hobbyists must begin to consider the possibility that breeding is not everything. My

This Ball Python, *P. regius*, is being probed to determine its sex. Probing is the most accurate, practical method for sexing snakes. Photo by I. Francais.

Housing male pythons together can be disastrous. This Reticulated Python, *P. reticulatus*, was seve·ely lacerated by another male and needed to be sutured. Photo by W. Allen, Jr.

suggestion would be to buy your python as a pet, handle it, and learn to understand it. Don't breed unless you have a carefully considered plan of how to get rid of hatchlings if you cannot sell them, and by that I don't mean abandoning them in the local park.

BASICS

Most common pythons are being bred in captivity by someone. Because almost all pythons have very similar requirements for breeding, it is possible to outline a basic breeding sequence that should work for most pythons. For details on the various species, refer to the individual species discussions.

To be breedable, pythons must be sexually mature. In most species pythons are adult by the age of three or four, and it is not uncommon for specimens well into their teens to breed successfully. The adults must be in excellent condition and able to survive a two-month cooling period without food. Females must have sufficient fat reserves to withstand the rigors of egg production and possibly brooding.

The sexes must be correctly determined. Few pythons can be sexed by external means. In most species both sexes have well-developed spurs, though they may be larger and darker in males than females, and it takes a very experienced eye to correctly guess sex by spur condition. Correct sexing usually requires probing of the pouches at the base of the cloaca and noting the depth of penetration. In almost all pythons, females probe to only the depth of three or four subcaudals, while males probe ten or more subcaudals.

All breeding stock must be

wormed before the breeding season and should be free of mites and ticks. Specimens showing any signs of respiratory diseases may not survive the cooling period.

COOLING

Though it really is not necessary, almost all breeding of pythons today is done following a two-month (roughly) period of cool temperature and shortened day lengths with reduced or no feeding. Many factors may spur reproduction in pythons, including those involved in cooling, but many zoos and private breeders have had good

This writhing mass is actually a pair of Australian Water Pythons, *Liasis fuscus*, mating. These animals are not commonly bred by hobbyists. Photo by K. H. Switak.

breeding success by just reducing day length from 14 to 10 hours, allowing two males to fight each other in the presence of females, or just separating and then reuniting the sexes. Cooling, however, provides a simple formula for breeding that almost

Here are the cloacal spurs of an approximately 90 cm/ 3 ft male Rough-spotted Python, *Antaresia maculosa*. The spurs of male pythons are usually larger than those of females. Photo by M. Walls.

always works and is easily duplicated year after year.

The well-conditioned, correctly sexed pythons are cooled separately. The temperature is allowed to drop by ten degrees Celsius over a period of two or three weeks. Most pythons can survive a couple of months at temperatures as low as 16°C (60°F), but 21°C (70°F) is more than adequate. Always provide water during the cooling period. Many keepers also provide a small basking light during the cooling period so specimens may bask if they feel they need the additional heat. At these temperatures pythons usually will not feed and may not be able to digest their food. They should go into the cooling period with empty guts.

Most breeders in the United States and Europe time the cooling period for the winter, which makes it easier to maintain low temperatures without artificial means.

After two months, the snakes slowly are brought back up to normal temperatures and longer days and started feeding again. When the sexes are put back together, mating should follow almost immediately or at least in a few weeks. Multiple matings would seem to assure a higher rate of fertilization.

LAYING

Females commonly lay their eggs six weeks to two months after mating, during the Northern Hemisphere spring. As you already know from the species discussions, different species of pythons lay eggs of different sizes and clutches of widely varying

This is a female Diamond Python, *P. s. spilotus*, laying a clutch of eggs. Notice some of the eggs are spindly shaped; these may not be fertile. Photo by K. H. Switak.

numbers. Often the fertile eggs are accompanied with numbers of infertile eggs that will decompose in a few weeks and should be removed.

In nature, most true pythons (Pythonidae) brood their egg clutches in the security of a burrow, a depression under a log, or some other hidden place. They coil about the eggs and help maintain the nest at a

This is an Australian Water Python, *Liasis fuscus*, coiled around her clutch of eggs. Photo by K. H. Switak.

constant temperature by using repeated tiny muscle shivers to release heat. Shivering generally takes place only when the temperature in the burrow drops more than two or three degrees below what the snake innately knows to be the correct temperature. Shivering is one of those little evolutionary developments that give a species just a tiny bit of advantage, perhaps allowing just one or two more eggs to hatch than would otherwise happen or perhaps letting the eggs hatch one or two days earlier than otherwise. In nature every small advantage may pay big dividends for the

survival of a species over thousands of years.

INCUBATION AND YOUNG

No commercial and few hobby breeders allow the mother to brood her eggs naturally. I am not sure why this is so, as it seems that letting nature do the work would be the best way. After all, the mother knows the temperature limits that are best for her eggs and also understands humidity requirements, which may vary greatly from species to species and are poorly understood by humans. Of course, it is simpler to handle eggs than to handle a very aggressive mother

Sphagnum moss is one of the most commonly used incubation media for python eggs. Photo by I. Francais.

python determined to protect her eggs from any outside attention. Many female pythons, by the way, continue to feed while brooding if food is offered, and in nature they may leave the nest during warm nights to hunt for food.

The eggs usually are incubated in moistened vermiculite. In most situations one part of vermiculite is mixed with one part of dechlorinated water (by weight, not volume). The incubation container must be large enough to house the entire clutch if the eggs are stuck together (as often is the case), and there must always be lots of vermiculite on all sides of the eggs except for a small exposed area that allows the egg to breathe. After the first few hours from laying, the eggs should not be turned or handled any more than necessary. Add water to the vermiculite as necessary to maintain the moisture and spray carefully on occasion.

Almost all python eggs do well at 32°C (90°F) or a degree or two cooler. Most python eggs have an incubation period of between 60 and 70 days, at which time the hatchlings will slit the shell with their egg tooth. Slitting may be followed by the emergence of the hatchling in a few hours, or it may stay in the shell for one or two days before coming out. Hatchlings have yolk stored in their guts and thus do not need a meal immediately. Most species shed their skin one or two weeks after leaving the egg, but a few species molt after just two or three days, and some may not have their first molt for a full month. Generally the hatchling is ready to feed shortly after the first molt, and breeders usually offer food at that time. If the hatchling is healthy but does not feed for the first month, there generally is no problem. After six weeks without feeding, you should consult an expert for suggestions on how best to

Newly hatched Carpet Pythons, *P. s. variegatus*, are not nearly as pretty as they will be after their first shed. Photo by P. Freed.

Striped Carpet Pythons, *P. s. variegatus*, are very rare animals. It is unknown whether striping is genetic in Carpet Pythons or a artifact from incubation. Photo by R. D. Bartlett.

force-feed the reluctant hatchling.

Some python babies feed readily, others never feed. Breeders try a variety of foods in addition to the standard rodents before resorting to force-feeding. Lizards and lizard-scented rodents often work. Infant mortalities are very high in some

Hatchling White-lipped Pythons, *Liasis albertisi*, are quite a challenge to rear. Photo by C. Banks.

species, and a few species have so far defied all attempts at repeated successful breeding.

Please remember that this chapter is a very simplified condensation of techniques that have proved to be reliable for most species and most breeders under most circumstances. Breeding any snake is an art, and not every hobbyist has the patience and the proper knack for the job. Don't be too disappointed if you do not have good luck at first. Most pythons will lay a clutch each year, so you will get a second chance soon enough. This will give you plenty of time to read detailed breeding accounts for your species (see the Further Reading section) and perhaps discuss your problems with a successful breeder or two. Successful breeding is based on practice, patience, and information, not just luck.

Green Burmese Pythons, *P. m. bivittatus*, are a popularly bred variety and have been crossed with amelanistics to generate tawny yellow animals. Photo by A. Both.

Thanks to Satan, the Blood Python, for his invaluable assistance. Photo by M. Walls. Courtesy S. and R. Mitchell.